CW00554905

GONE WITH THE WIND.

Demolition of Gamnel Wharf windmill, Tring, 4th May, 1911.

GONE WITH THE WIND:
WINDMILLS, AND THOSE AROUND TRING

Ian Petticrew

and

Wendy Austin

TRING
MMX

First published 2010
© Ian Petticrew and
Wendy Austin 2010

All rights reserved.
No part of this publication may be reproduced,
stored in a retrieval system, or transferred
in any form or by any means, electronic,
mechanical, photocopying, recording,
or otherwise, without the prior
permission of the authors.

Front cover: Gamnel Wharf windmill, Tring.

ISBN
978-0-9537924-7-4

Printed by
think*ink*
11-13 Philip Road, Ipswich, Suffolk, IP2 8BH

TO THE MEMORY OF THE

MILLWRIGHTS AND THE MILLERS

WHO BUILT AND OPERATED THESE

POWERHOUSES OF THE PAST

AND TO THOSE WHO HAVE TOILED

TO RESTORE THE FEW THAT REMAIN.

CONTENTS

ILLUSTRATIONS

COLOUR PLATES

FOREWORD

Fascination with windmills has led to the publication of many books on the subject. Some concentrate on their design, equipment and machinery; others on their history; and some express in words and pictures their supposedly 'romantic' side. Although one would not argue that a windmill standing on a distant skyline, its slowly-revolving sails glinting in the sunlight, must have *appeared* romantic, any romance in the life of the miller is not borne out by the facts; his was taxing and sometimes dangerous work, as well as being a business subject to the vagaries of the weather and the commodity market.

Windmilling was to suffer a rapid decline from the mid-19th century as more modern production methods took over. Of those windmills that survived, most became private dwellings or static exhibits, but a few were restored to full working order, such as the tower mill at Quainton in Buckinghamshire.

This book touches on each of these aspects of the subject, although that was *not* the original plan. The idea first arose from an interest in local history and the simple wish to place on record the windmills in and around the town of Tring in Hertfordshire. But it soon became apparent that certain peripheral explanations were needed in order to help the uninformed reader understand the subject more fully. Thus, our original intention grew until it covered, in brief, most facets of windmilling, including a section on literary allusions to windmills.

Books of this sort always rely heavily on what has previously been written by others more versed in the subject. This is particularly so with windmills, for of those that remain, few are in operation. Our thanks are therefore due to earlier writers whose research paved the way, especially to Stanley Freese (1902-72), an author who wrote much about the subject during the 1930s and beyond when more windmills remained - although often in a derelict condition - and when their heyday was still within living memory.

We acknowledge with gratitude the help of those who gave their time to review our text, supply information, lend photographs, and invite us into their windmills and homes: especially to Michael Bass, Catherine Bushell, Sandra Costello, Tom Derbyshire, Mary and Michelle Evans, Jill Fowler, Liz Griffin, Diane and Stewart Ivory, Terry and Jill Jenkins, Kate and Peter Hoskin, Linda McGhee, Peter Keeley, Paul Messenger, Heather Pratt, Ann Reed, Keith Russell, Peter Mayne and Alasdair Simpson.

We are also grateful to the staff at the Centre for Buckinghamshire Local Studies who, as always, have been patient and helpful in dealing with our enquiries while researching this book, and to The Hertfordshire Record Office, Cholesbury & St Leonards Local History Society, and Pitstone Local History Society.

The authors stress that neither is a professed expert on windmills nor on any aspect of grain milling past or present. Thus, we hope that readers will forgive any errors which, despite careful checking and review, have crept into the text.

I.S.P. and W.M.A.
Tring, 2010

INTRODUCTION

Ever since man ceased to be a hunter gatherer and settled down to a predominantly agrarian existence, the grinding of grain has been a central feature of rural life. From the simple quern stones of the Neolithic Age through the age of the water-, wind- and steam-driven mills, to the electrically-powered, computer-controlled, roller mills of the present day, the production of flour has remained essential to the preparation of our most basic food, the loaf of bread.

The Romans are believed to have first brought watermills to our country. A thousand years later, many places recorded in the Domesday Book had one or more *mills*, most probably run by water power. Tring's Domesday entry records two mills, both valued at 9s.0d. Within the Tring Hundred, several more are listed: one at Tiscott, value 10s.0d.; two at Puttenham, value 10s.8d.; one at Gubblecote, value 12s.4d.; and one at Wigginton, value 5s.0d. Given the latter's hilltop position and low valuation, this was probably a mill driven by a single or a pair of yoked oxen. And for hundreds of years, small hand-operated grinding stones were used in many rural homes.

Although there is a reference to a windmill in Persia as far back as AD 644, the first known practical windmills in that country date from the 10th century. Such early examples took the form of a roofless tower supporting a vertical pole to which lightweight sails were attached to horizontal struts. This type of windmill was known as a 'panemone' and was fixed in one position. The concept is thought to have been brought to Northern Europe by knights returning from the Crusades in the

Middle East; the first mention of a windmill in Europe is in a Papal Bull of 1105. The idea then spread throughout the Low Countries, Denmark, and Bohemia, in fact to any location lacking water to drive a mill but where there was plenty of wind energy.[1] The great Mongol conqueror, Ghengis Khan, also realized the wind's potential as a source of power, and following his invasion of Persia he took local millers back to China to build identical mills.

Figure 0.1 Detail from the 'Walsokne Brass' plaque (1349).

The first references to windmills in Britain date from the last quarter of the 12th century, but surviving pictorial evidence is much later. One of the earliest illustrations is that on the 'Walsokne Brass' plaque in St. Margaret's Church, Kings Lynn. Dating from 1349, a panel at the foot of the brass depicts a horseman carrying grain to be ground at a windmill, followed by two men who are bearing their lord on a litter (*fig. 0.1*). The type of windmill shown is a wooden structure known as a *tripod post mill*, in which a substantial upright post supported the main body of the mill, the upright post being braced by supporting beams forming a tripod arrangement. This

---

[1] Water mills have always existed in greater numbers. A flow of water can be controlled more precisely to provide the thrust required by the gearwork inside the mill. Wind, on the other hand, does not always blow and when it does, its velocity and direction can change at any moment.

construction enabled the mill to be rotated around the post to face the wind. The sails were covered in cloth and the wind power thus captured drove a single pair of grinding stones. This type of windmill continued with minor modifications and improvements until the $17^{th}/18^{th}$ centuries, by which time windmill construction had evolved into more sophisticated and substantial smock and tower mills.

The Industrial Revolution began in Britain around the mid-18th century and led to a gradual transition from an agrarian to a manufacturing economy. Until this period, most of our population lived in the countryside in small communities that were much more self-contained than those to which we are now accustomed, and which relied on the local grain mill for the production of both human and animal foodstuff. By the beginning of the 19th century it is estimated that there were some 10,000 grain mills of various types operating in Britain. As well as grinding cereals, windmills were used for a variety of other purposes including, in East Anglia and other low-lying areas, the pumping of excess water into drainage ditches.

By the middle of the 19th century, the arrival of steam power together with more modern milling techniques rendered wind and water mills obsolete and they fell rapidly into decline. Some survived as private dwellings, some as static museum exhibits and a few were even restored to working order by dedicated preservationists; but the vast majority simply fell into decay and were eventually demolished.

We are fortunate that in Tring and the surrounding area, four of the five windmills whose histories are given in this book survive. Pitstone Windmill, now fully restored and preserved as an historic monument, is cared for by the National Trust. The other three have been converted to private dwellings at Tring (Goldfield), at Wendover and on Hawridge Common. The fifth, Gamnel Wharf windmill at Tring, was pulled down in 1911; although the only one of the five local windmills not to survive, its site, ironically, is now occupied by one of the largest flour mills in the country.

A little further afield, but not described in detail (*see Chapter 13*), are examples of post mills at Brill and at Chinnor, a smock mill at Lacey Green and a tower mill at Quainton. There is also a tower mill at Edlesborough - alas, not visible from the road - that has been converted into a holiday home, while a short distance away is Doolittle Mill, a rare example of a *combined* wind and water mill, now an attractive private dwelling. And not to disregard completely the competing technology, there are working water mills in the locality at Ford End (Ivinghoe) and Redbournbury (St. Albans). Both are open to the public, the latter producing bread for sale in its adjoining bakery.

Chapter 1

WHO OWNS THE WIND?

Much surrounding the answer to this interesting question stems from the meaning of the archaic word 'soke'.

At the time of the Norman Conquest, soke generally meant 'jurisdiction'. Thus, during the medieval period, mills of all types were governed by 'milling soke'. In other words a mill was the property of the feudal lord of the manor, who gained a monopoly over milling and his tenants were bound to grind their corn at the mill at a fixed rate of toll. This was usually one sixteenth of the corn ground, but the rate varied.

Moving on to this apparently absurd question of 'who owns the wind?' we find a long legal pedigree. Under feudal law anyone could construct or erect a windmill on his heritage, *provided* that it was not within the jurisdiction of a lord possessing manorial milling soke rights; within the manor, a windmill's owner (the lord of the manor) possessed the right to use all wind necessary to drive his mill and thus became, *de facto*, "owner of the wind".

At the extinction of milling soke, the monopoly of corn-grinding and thus ownership of the wind disappeared, but not quite. If an ancient prescriptive right already existed, the monopoly protecting the mill from any interference with its aerial motive-power - for example by erecting buildings or planting trees in the close vicinity - might continue by Act of

Parliament. Thus, a clause from the Act for the enclosure of the Wavertree Common Lands near Liverpool, whereon stood an ancient soke mill: *"If any person or persons shall erect or build any house or building, or shall plant any tree or trees within the distance of two hundred yards from a certain windmill situate on the common, or shall suffer any tree or trees planted without the distance aforesaid to grow to such a height as to prevent the going of the said windmill, the same shall be and is hereby declared a nuisance, and shall and may be removed or prevented by the said lord of the manor or the owner or occupier of the said windmill."*

Legal cases concerning ownership of the wind arose until well into the 19th century. In 1861 a plaintiff, who since 1856 had owned a windmill built in 1829, claimed a right to enjoy the benefit of the currents of air from the west. The defendant had interfered with this right by building a school-house only 25 yards from the mill that impeded all westerly air currents from reaching the mill, thus causing a loss of £300, and an injunction was sought restraining the defendants from continuing the injury. But the case failed for no very clear reasons, although it seems that the crux of the problem was that the claimant wanted the whole of the defendant's property pulled down, rather than just sufficient part of it. This contrasts with another case of similar date in which the owner of a windmill, similarly impeded, and recognising that his was not an ancient mill covered by prescriptive rights, adopted the pragmatic strategy of dodging the impediment by raising the windmill by another 30 feet.

With the proliferation of wind turbines, similar cases involving 'ownership of the wind' might well re-emerge.

Chapter 2

TYPES OF WINDMILL

Setting aside prairie wind pumps, wind turbines and other recent developments, traditional windmills fall into three broad categories, the 'post mill', the 'smock mill' and the 'tower mill'.

Post Mills

Post mills were the earliest type of windmill to reach Britain, probably late in the 12th century. They are so named because the body of the mill is supported on and revolves around an upright *post*. This enables the mill to be turned to face into the wind - a task called *winding* or *luffing* - where its sails can generate the most torque.[2] Many examples remain throughout Western Europe, those at Pitstone (*plate 1*), at Brill (*plate 4*) and at Chinnor (*plate 7*) being nearest to Tring.

The mill's supporting post needs to be a substantial piece of timber to carry the weight of the mill's superstructure and machinery. That which supports Pitstone mill was cut from a single tree, some 17 feet long by 33 inches diameter at its base, comparable in girth to a sailing ship's mast. The post is capped with a bearing, which permits rotation - via the *tail pole* at the rear (*fig. 2.1*) - and supports the full weight of the mill through a massive wooden cross-beam called the *crown tree* (*fig. 2.2*).

---

[2] A 'twisting' force.

3

In *fig. 2.2*, the post appears to rest upon the *cross-trees* beneath it, but this is not so. Were it to be, the entire weight of the mill would bear down on their centre, which would eventually fracture under the pressure. Thus, the post is suspended slightly above the cross-trees by four *quarter bars*, which are mortised into it and which also maintain its vertical position. By this means the mill's weight is transferred downwards through the quarter bars to the four brick *piers*. The cross-trees, which are held in a permanent state of tension by the outward thrust of the mill's weight, prevent the quarter posts from spreading, a clever resolution of forces.

Figure 2.1 The post mill that stood on Bledlow Ridge near Chinnor. It was demolished in 1933.

4

Many post mills eventually had a brick *roundhouse* built about their base (*plates 1 and 4*) to protect their timber supports from the weather and to provide a covered loading bay.

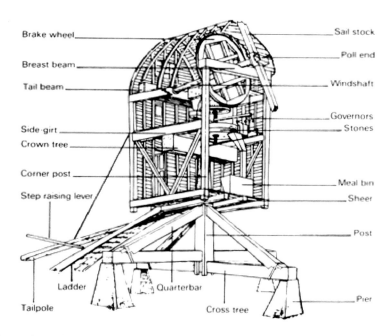

Figure 2.2 The weight of a post mill is transferred through the four quarter bars to the brick piers on which they rest.

Smock Mills

Due to its distinctive sloping sides, usually six or eight in number, this type of windmill came to be named after the canvas and cotton smocks worn by farm labourers of the time. As with the earlier post mill, the sides of a smock mill are clad with horizontal weatherboarding, although there are some

5

examples of vertical cladding. The mill's wooden body sits on a brick base to protect it against rot and to provide support for its upright posts. The base can be a substantial structure, that supporting Union Mill (*fig. 2.3*) being a four-storey building.

Figure 2.3 Union Mill, Cranbrook, Kent, Britain's tallest smock mill. It was built in 1814 and is now open to the public.

The main internal structure of a smock mill consists of its *cant* or corner posts (*plate 11*), which extend to its full height, converging as they go up. The cant posts are secured at the bottom to a wooden sill, which is fixed firmly to the brick base. This joint between post and sill poses a problem; because the cant posts lean inwards they throw the mill's weight outwards at the sill, where a weak joint can result in posts slipping away and toppling the mill.

6

Unlike the post mill, in which the whole body of the mill needs to be turned to wind its sails, only the top - or *cap* - of a smock mill needs to rotate. The small cap also allows better airflow around the sails, which contributes to a more efficient and stable source of power, especially when winding is performed automatically by a small windmill known as a *fantail (plate 26)*. And because the body of the mill is static, it can be larger than a post mill, thus allowing more space for machinery.

Smock mills are found throughout Western Europe; in the U.K. they were particularly common in Kent. The nearest smock mill to Tring is at Lacey Green near Princes Risborough *(plate 10)*.

Tower mills

The earliest record of a tower mill in Britain dates from the late 13th century and refers to a mill at Dover, possibly at the Castle. In that age, windmills were sometimes built on the sides of castles and of towers in fortified towns to protect them from attack.

The tower mill differs from the smock mill in that it is of brick or stone construction and usually round in shape, although there is a fine example of an octagonal tower mill at Wendover *(plate 22)*. Because of its masonry construction, a tower mill requires increasingly massive walls towards its base to support the weight of the upper storeys; those at Wendover mill are three feet thick at the base. It is therefore unsurprising that tower mills were much more expensive to construct than wooden post and smock mills, and probably for this reason they did not become prevalent until the 18th and 19th centuries.

However, this type of construction offers the advantage of a more robust frame that can support larger sails and resist harsher weather.

In common with the smock mill, the tower mill is topped by a moveable cap, that at Stembridge Tower Mill at High Ham, Somerset, being the last example of a thatched cap.

The nearest tower mill to Tring is Goldfield Mill (*plate 19*) on Icknield Way, near to the junction with Miswell Lane. Slightly further afield are examples of tower mills at Hawridge (*plate 15*) and at Wendover. These three mills have been converted into private

Figure 2.4 Quainton tower mill prior to restoration.

dwellings, but the tower mill at Quainton has been restored to working order and is open to the public.

Chapter 3

HOW A WINDMILL WORKS

Introduction

Little change occurred in windmill design from their first use in Britain until the Industrial Revolution, when a number of significant advances were made in the design of sails and machinery. But important though they were, these advances were slow to gain acceptance and too late to make a significant impact, for by then James Watt's condensing steam engine was in the ascendant. From about the mid-19th century, steam-powered milling began rapidly to supplant wind and water power. This was followed by the introduction of industrial-scale flour mills in which steel rollers replaced grindstones to produce, in greater quantity, finer and more consistent quality products. Mead's (later Heygates) Flour Mill at Tring (*Chapter 8*) is an early example of an industrial-scale flour mill.

This chapter describes the general operation of a windmill and some of the advances in design that were made towards the end of the windmill era. A brief description of the modern *roller mill* is given in the Appendix.

What a windmill does

The mill was the first engine invented by man. For centuries, mills driven by water or wind were the only machines that could convert the power of nature into useful work. In the case of the windmill, wind striking its sails exerts a force upon them

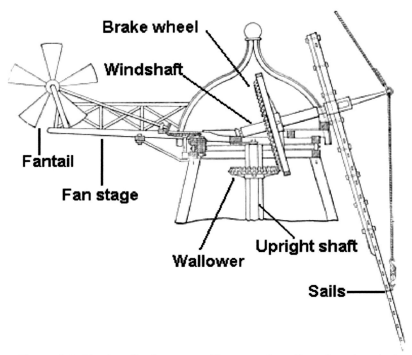

Figure 3.1 The fantail of a tower mill rotates the sails to face the wind.

that causes the shaft to which they are attached to rotate. What then follows depends on what task the windmill is to perform. Windmills have been used for many purposes, such as pumping water, sawing wood and as crushing machines in the preparation of oil, paper, spices, chalk and pottery. Today, wind turbines are used increasingly to generate electricity. But in Britain, the windmill's most common use over the centuries was to grind grain.

In a grain mill, the wind's energy, harnessed by the windmill's sails, is transferred via a system of shafts, cogs and belts to

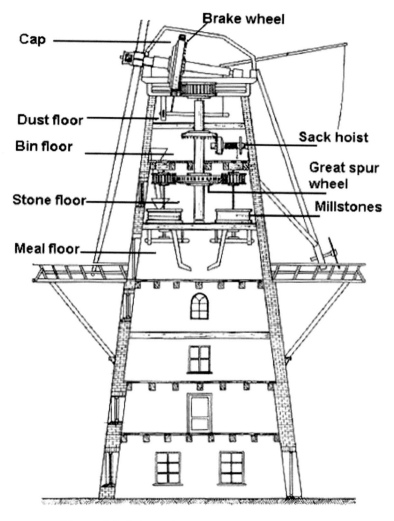

Figure 3.2 Schematic diagram of a tower mill.

drive one or more pairs of *millstones*. Grain, fed between the rotating millstones, is ground into *meal*.

The remainder of this chapter describes the main steps in the windmilling process; also the sails and machinery that are usually found within a windmill.

The floors of a windmill

Windmills do not follow a common design but they do share common features, not least of which is that windmilling is a gravity-driven process. Milling begins at the top of mill and each succeeding stage of the process is performed on the next floor down (in following this process the need for a *sack hoist* - for hoisting sacks of grain and meal up several floors of a windmill - soon becomes clear!)

Windmills were built with different numbers of floors,[3] hence, the windmilling process is not always exactly as described below. However, in general the following applies . . . .

    i.   The uppermost part of a windmill (*fig. 3.1*) houses the *windshaft*, bearings, cogs and the top of the *upright shaft*, which transmits the windshaft's rotary motion down through the mill to drive the machinery;

   ii.   The *dust floor* (*fig.3.2*), positioned under the *cap*, serves to keep dirt from above from falling into the storage bins and to keep dust rising up from below;

---

[3] That at *fig. 3.2* has additional floors for storage and living accommodation.

iii. The *bin floor* houses bins in which are stored grain for cleaning; cleaned grain for milling; and *meal* to be sifted;

iv. The *stone floor* houses grain-cleaning machinery, the *millstones* used to grind the grain, and machinery to sift the ground meal into various grades of fineness;

v. The *meal floor* houses chutes from the stone floor above, down which (depending on the stage of the milling process, described next) flows cleaned grain for milling, meal for sifting, and milled products, each of which is collected in sacks.

The milling process

The first step in the milling process is to hoist the grain to be milled up to the bin floor where it is loaded into a storage bin ready to be cleaned. When required, the uncleaned grain is discharged down a chute to the stone floor, where it is mechanically cleaned, then discharged down a chute for collection on the meal floor.

Sacks of cleaned grain are hoisted up the mill to the bin floor, where they are stored in a bin ready for milling. When required, the cleaned grain is discharged down a chute into a *hopper* on the stone floor, from where it is trickled into the millstones, ground and discharged down chutes for collection on the meal floor.

The sacks are then hoisted up the mill to the bin floor, from where the meal travels downwards, this time through a *flour dresser*, which sorts and distributes it according to its fineness, (white flour being the finest, *bran* the coarsest). All this machinery is powered by the thrust of the wind as harnessed by the windmill's sails.

The sails

A windmill's sails are usually four in number, but five, six and eight-sailed windmills (*fig 3.3*) were also built. More sails generate more power with a smoother torque, but at greater cost, weight and maintenance.

A windmill's sails do not rotate in the vertical plane, but are slightly inclined to it, for it was discovered that a slight inclination of about 15° increases the wind's effect (*fig. 3.4*). This is due to wind currents near to the ground meeting more frictional resistance than higher up, to the extent that at a level of 43

Figure 3.3 Leach's Mill, Wisbech.

ft above ground-level, wind velocity is some 10 per cent greater than at 20 ft. To accommodate the tilt of the sails, the windshaft has also to be inclined at the same angle below the horizontal, with its rear end held in place by a firmly-embedded bearing to enable it to rotate while preventing it from sliding backwards (*plates 17 and 25*).

14

A further discovery was that sails worked more efficiently if, rather than being set flat across the sail stock, a slight twist is applied, this being more accentuated nearest the windshaft (about 18°) lessening towards the tip (about 7°); this twist can be seen in the sails of Quainton mill (*plate 26*).

A major problem for the miller was to regulate the speed of rotation of the sails and thus of the millstones. The optimum sail speed for a grain mill generally lies in the range 11 to 15 revolutions per minute; speeds much above that run the risk of over-driving the stones and burning the grain, while even higher speeds - sometimes referred to as the mill 'running away' - could damage the machinery and, indeed, the mill itself.

Figure 3.4 Flow of air currents near to the ground.

Small differences in sail speed can be adjusted by changing the amount of grain fed to the millstones or changing the gap between them, both of which affect the load placed on the sails.

But a large change in wind speed has to be dealt with by altering the sail area exposed to the wind, either by increasing or reducing it, a process called *reefing* (*fig. 3.5*).

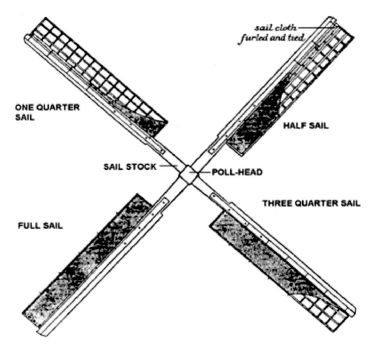

Figure 3.5 Different degrees of reefing a simple cloth-covered sail.

For centuries before the development of more advanced and better controlled sail systems, sails comprised a lattice framework over which the sailcloth was spread (*plate 10*). Such *common sails* required two men for reefing, one to climb on the sweeps to carry out the task and one to control the brake; should the brake fail during the operation, the man on the sweep was in for a spectacular ride.

Towards the end of the 18th century, developments in sail design eased the reefing process. *Roller reefing* employed banks of cloth blinds mounted on rollers (comparable to a household roller blind) that could be adjusted with a manual chain from the ground without stopping the mill. Other systems replaced the sailcloth with sets of wooden shutters (comparable to Venetian blinds) mounted along each sweep. These systems employed some form of tensioning that caused the shutters to spill the wind automatically if its force exceeded a set limit. A later invention, the *air brake (fig. 3.6)*, comprised shutters placed longitudinally at the tip of each sweep that turned automatically if the wind exceeded a set strength, thereby disturbing the sail's profile and slowing it.

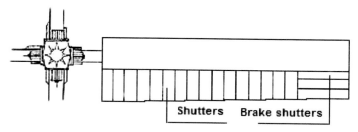

Figure 3.6 Sail fitted with shutters and air brake.

The development of hollow windshafts permitted control rods to be inserted through their centre *(fig. 3.7)*. This enabled sail settings to be adjusted from within the mill automatically under the action of counter-weights.

While these developments were not without their complexities when compared to common sails, they reduced manual effort while improving the windmill's efficiency as a motive force.

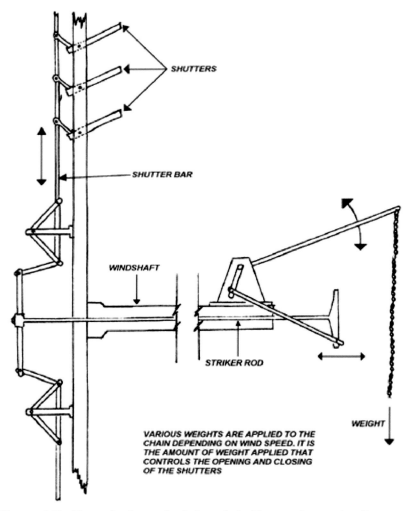

SHUTTERS

SHUTTER BAR

WINDSHAFT

STRIKER ROD

VARIOUS WEIGHTS ARE APPLIED TO THE
CHAIN DEPENDING ON WIND SPEED. IT IS
THE AMOUNT OF WEIGHT APPLIED THAT
CONTROLS THE OPENING AND CLOSING
OF THE SHUTTERS

WEIGHT

Figure 3.7 Towards the end of the windmill era, shuttered sails were introduced that enabled a degree of automatic reefing by applying tensioning weights to balance the wind pressure falling on the shutters. The two forces were balanced through the *striker rod* (passes through the centre of the *windshaft*), the *shutter bars* and movable linkages/levers.

18

The machinery

Different hardwoods were used in the construction of milling machinery. Cogs were often of applewood, hornbeam or beech, wheels and shafts of oak, whilst the dowels used to join together wooden parts were of holly. However, from the middle of the 18th century cast iron parts were used increasingly, although iron-to-iron gearing was avoided for it was found that iron-to-wood gearing ran more quietly and was easier and cheaper to maintain. Problems associated with manufacturing and handling large iron castings were avoided by the use of small sections bolted together, an example being the dozen or so sections that make up the 18ft diameter iron rack in the cap of Wendover mill (*plate 24*).

In order to rotate the millstones, the (near) horizontal rotation of the windshaft must first be converted into a vertical rotation. This is achieved using a form of bevel gearing. The inner end of the windshaft is fitted with a large toothed wheel, the *brake wheel*, the teeth of which mesh with a cog, the *wallower*, which is set at an upright angle to it. The brake wheel, when rotated by the windmill's sails in the horizontal, causes the wallower to rotate in the vertical (*fig. 3.8*).

The wallower is mounted on the *upright (or main) shaft*, which transmits its rotary motion downwards through the mill. Mounted on the base of the upright shaft is another large toothed wheel, the *great spur wheel*. This in turn meshes with the cogs - called *stone nuts* - that drive the millstones. In this way the wind's energy is captured and then put to work to grind grain and drive other machinery for cleaning, sifting and hoisting grain.

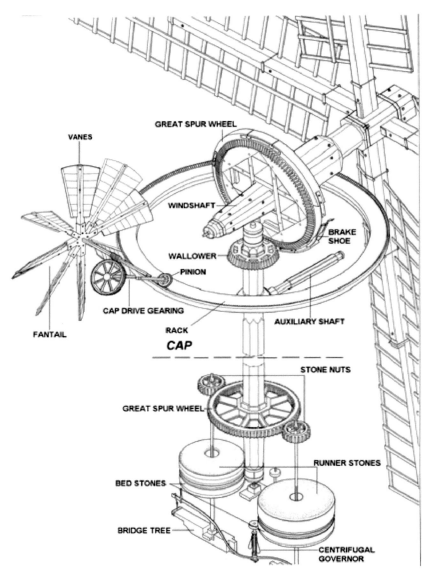

Figure 3.8 General arrangement of a windmill built with a cap.

As its name implies, the brake wheel's other function is to stop the mill. In *fig. 3.8*, the brake is the circular shoes that surround the brake wheel. To stop the mill, a lever is pulled to tighten the brake-shoes causing them to grip the periphery of the brake wheel and thus slow the rotating windshaft or clamp it in place.

The millstones

Windmills are generally equipped with several sets of millstones. Each set comprises a rotating *runner stone* and a stationary *bed stone* which, depending on their diameter, weigh in the region of two tons. Different types of stone are used to grind different types of grain. Stones of grey millstone grit from Derbyshire are used to grind coarse meal for stock feeding. The millstones employed to grind wheat for flour are made of French Burr, a hard silicate found in the Seine valley. Burr stones are constructed in segments, cemented together and bound with heavy iron bands.

In operation, the millstones (*fig. 3.9*) are fed from a hopper, which trickles grain along a wooden trough - the *shoe* - into the *eye* (a hole through the centre of the runner stone) where it is ground between runner and bed stones. The shoe is kept in a continual state of agitation by a rotating crank. Called the *damsel*, due to its chattering sound when in operation, it serves to keep the grain flowing steadily down the shoe into the eye.

Each stone has a pattern of grooves cut into its surface. The grooves act like scissors, cutting the grain as well as moving it outwards from the centre to the periphery of the millstones. As the meal emerges from between the stones, it is swept inside the circular wooden container that encases them - the *tun* or *stone case* - into the top of a chute, or meal-spout, which funnels it down to the meal floor below where it is bagged.

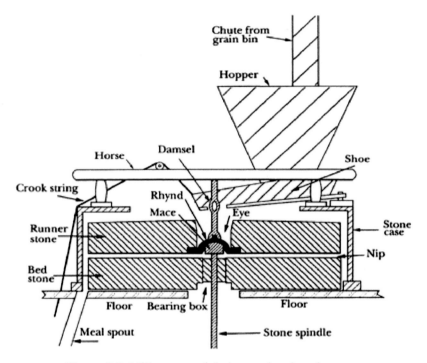

Figure 3.9 Millstones and their associated equipment.

In regular use the grooves wear down and need to be *dressed* periodically; that is, re-cut to keep their cutting surfaces sharp. This is a tedious and exacting task, sometimes performed by the miller but often by an itinerant stone dresser. The work was executed using various tools including a *mill bill* (*fig. 3.11*), a tempered steel blade clamped in a wooden handle, rather like a small pickaxe, and used as a chipping tool. Today, power tools are often used.

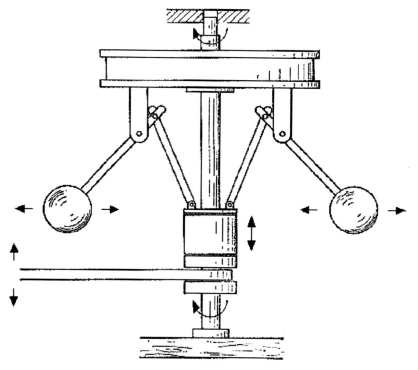

Figure 3.10 The centrifugal governor.

Adjusting the gap between the stones - a process called *tentering* - is carried out using a system of screws or levers that move the runner stone up or down. This gap, or *nip* as millers call it, helps to determine the fineness of the meal; the smaller the nip, the finer the meal. Only slight adjustments are required, for the stones, when grinding, are only about the thickness of a postcard apart.

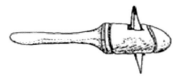

Figure 3.11 A 'mill bill'.

Tentering can be performed manually, but the *centrifugal governor* (*fig. 3.10*) can perform the task more efficiently. This ingenious device is driven from the rotating upright shaft. As the speed of rotation of the sails - and thus of the shaft and the millstones - increases, a pair of heavy metal balls linked to the governor's spindle begin to fly outwards under the increasing centrifugal force. This causes their collar to rise up the spindle, and in so doing to move the levers that adjust the gap between the millstones. An increased gap results in more grain being fed into the eye of the millstones, which increases the load on the sails, slowing their speed of rotation and that of the millstones.

The optimum speed of rotation of a runner stone depends on its diameter and on the quality of the output required. A rule of thumb followed by millers was to divide the diameter of the stone (in inches) into 5,000 for flour and 6,000 for coarser meal. Thus the optimum speed for a 48 inch runner stone, set to produce meal, would be 125 rpm - assuming of course that the wind would drive it at that speed.

The fantail

Even a small change in wind direction can result in a significant reduction in the torque the sails generate if they are not repositioned. In older windmills, 'winding the mill' involved hard manual effort. In the case of a post mill, the entire superstructure needed to be turned by pushing on a large beam (the *tail post*) that protruded from the rear of the mill. In later smock and tower mills, only the top floor (*fig. 3.1*) needs to revolve, but this still required manual effort. The fantail automates the process by using the wind itself to wind the sails. Later windmills usually adopted this feature, which could also be built onto the tail posts of old post mills.

A fantail comprises gearing driven by a small set of sails (*vanes*), which are aligned at right angles to the main sails and positioned at the rear of the mill. Its purpose is to rotate the cap automatically when a change of wind direction occurs, which it achieves via a system of gears that mesh with a toothed rack around the inside of the cap (*fig. 3.8*). When the sails are properly winded, the vanes of the fantail are at right angles to the wind and do not rotate. But should the wind change direction, its force then begins to fall to one or the other side of the fantail causing its vanes to rotate. These in turn drive the gearing that rotates the cap and winds the sails, a clever feat of automation.

However, while very useful in normal working conditions, the fantail provided no guarantee against a mill being *tail-winded* by a sudden change in wind direction, as sometimes accompanies a thunderstorm; thus fantails might be supplemented by a hand crank, an example being in the cap of Wendover mill. And unless the fantail drive could be disconnected, a further problem for the miller was how to turn the windmill's sails off the wind in a sudden squall in order to stop them. Nothing was ever straight-forward in windmilling.

Ancillary equipment

Because windmills use gravity feed to clean and grind grain, filter the meal produced and bag the end product, a *sack hoist* is an essential piece of equipment if the drudgery of lifting sacks manually up the mill, on numerous occasions, is to be avoided. The sack hoist takes the form a simple rotating chain, driven by an auxiliary shaft which is in turn geared to the upright shaft (*plate 3*). As it rotates, the sack hoist is used to lift the sacks of grain or meal up through a succession of trapdoors to the bin floor of the mill.

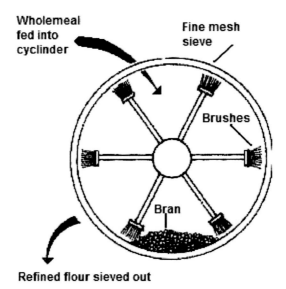

Figure 3.12 Principle of the flour dresser. The cylinder is tilted at an angle, the wholemeal being fed into the upper end and passing through the machine under gravity, the bran being ejected at the lower end.

The auxiliary shaft also powers other windmill machinery. That used before grain is milled might include a *smutter*, which removes the black spots of smut caused by a fungus disease that can grow on grain if its gets damp; a *separator*, used to separate grain from other foreign matter, such as stones, weeds, and sticks; a *scourer*, used to separate usable grain from debris such as dirt, dust, and chaff.

Following milling, a *flour dresser* (*fig. 3.12*) is used to sift the meal into its various grades of fineness. The dresser consists of a cylindrical drum, covered in wire mesh of increasing grades of fineness, and set at an angle. Inside the drum revolves a set of brushes. Meal, fed into the upper end of the cylinder is rubbed against the mesh screens by the brushes as it passes through the cylinder under gravity. The finest meal, white flour, can pass through the finest mesh screen; next comes semolina flour, which passes through the next grade of mesh, leaving the coarsest product, bran. Each grade is ejected into canvas chutes which feed sacks on the meal floor below.

The mill might also drive an *oat crusher*, used to crush oats for animal feed.

APPENDIX: the roller mill

Although the subject of this book is windmills, some mention should be made of the technology that in the latter part of the 19th century was to sweep away both wind and water mills so rapidly.

The steam engine was the first major advance. The first steam-powered mill, Albion Mill, was established in 1786 by Matthew Boulton and James Watt. It employed a Watt steam engine of 150 hp to drive 20 pairs of millstones, and was capable of grinding 10 bushels of wheat per hour, all day and regardless of wind strength. Albion Mill was the industrial wonder of the age, but in 1791 it burned down. The cause was never discovered, but it was widely believed to be an act of arson by local millers and millworkers who believed their livelihood was threatened by the new technology.

Rotating millstones, sometimes steam-driven, continued to be used for grain milling until the late 19th century, when roller mills - a Swiss invention - appeared, the first being built in Hungary in 1874. Edward Mead (*Chapter 8*) is believed to have installed the UK's first roller mill at Chelsea in 1881. The combination of steam power and the roller milling process led directly to the flour mills of today.

Roller milling (*fig. 3.13*) crushes the grain, not between revolving millstones, but between a series of fluted steel rollers of about 12 inches in diameter. The rollers are set with a specified gap between them and spin towards each other at high, but at different, speeds; the surface of each roller is also grooved with a different pattern.

In a modern flour mill, before milling commences, the grain is cleaned of any extraneous matter using a variety of techniques including sifters and magnets (to remove metallic particles). It is then conditioned to ensure uniform moisture content and blended with other wheats to provide a mix capable of producing flour of the required character. Then, using a reduction process, the grain is crushed by a succession of rollers, the fine flour particles being sifted out at each pass of the rollers while the residue (bran) is sent on to the next set of rollers in a repetitive manner. Thus, roller milling is a series of crushing and sifting operations, ideally suited for making clean white flour.

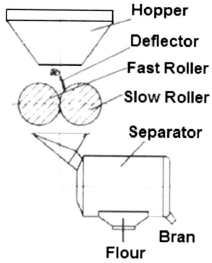

Figure 3.13 The principle of the roller mill. In practice, the meal passes through several stages of roller milling to produce flour.

Roller mills offer several other advantages over traditional milling methods. They eliminate the cost of dressing millstones and enable the production of a larger amount of better-grade flour from a given amount of wheat, quicker and to a consistent standard. Rollers are also superior for milling the harder wheats used for bread by reducing the wheat kernel slowly into flour fragments to separate out the bran.

Roller milling made possible the construction of larger, more efficient grain mills, hastening the abandonment of the small country wind and water mills, and of stone grinding. Indeed, so successful were the roller mills that within 30 years of their introduction into Britain in 1881, more than three-quarters of the wind and water mills that had served for centuries so faithfully, if erratically, had been demolished or abandoned. This is what Edward Bradfield, an old miller who was writing in 1920, had to say about this milling revolution . . . .

"Then came the changes. 'High grinding,' 'gradual reduction' and the 'roller system', one after the other, came to revolutionize the trade. The flour was greatly improved by the new methods and the trade of the stone millers was decimated. The new methods allowed the brittle stony wheats then coming into fame to be made into excellent flour which the stone millers could not equal. Yet many of them, who clung to the traditional system which had brought them fame, wealth and honour, made heroic efforts to stay the onslaught, but failed."

However, the roller mill revolution brought with it a drawback. The friction of the rollers caused the meal to become hot, which led to some nutrients in the flour being damaged. This was not realized at a time when essential dietary needs were little understood.

Today, the "Bread and Flour Regulations" govern the use of additives as well as requiring the addition of certain nutrients to ensure that a wholesome product emerges from the flour mill. This from the Federation of Bakers . . . . .

"The Bread and Flour Regulations require that flour should contain not less than 0.24mg. thiamin (vitamin B1), 1.60mg. nicotinic acid and 1.65mg. of iron per 100g. of flour. These amounts are found naturally in wholemeal flour. White and brown flours must be fortified to restore their nutritional value to the required level. In addition calcium carbonate, at a level of not less than 235mg. and not more than 390mg. per 100g. of flour, is added to all flours except wholemeal and certain self-raising varieties. This ensures the high nutritional value of all bread, whether it is white, brown or wholemeal."

Chapter 4

THE MILLER

A cheat?

The Victorian image of the 'hale and bold' miller, who 'wrought and sang from morn till night', was a romantic depiction. Although the miller was a necessary member of our former rural communities, he was often unpopular. Far from being the jolly red-faced figure, clad in a dusty apron and with a song upon his lips, the villagers often regarded him as cantankerous, mean-spirited and sometimes a cheat. This view can be attributed in part to Geoffrey Chaucer who, writing at the end of the 14th century, bequeathed to millers for the next 500 years a reputation for dishonesty that was undoubtedly supported by at least a grain of truth.

In *The Reeve's Tale*, Chaucer depicts a coarse and lewd man, who was often violent in the bargain . . . .

> *"A rumbustious cheat of sixteen stone*
> *Big in brawn, and big in bone,*
> *He was a master hand at stealing grain*
> *And often took three times his due*
> *Because of feeling with his thumb,*
> *He knew its quality.*
> *By God! To think it went by rote,*
> *A golden thumb to judge an oat!"*

Wealthier than the ordinary folk, the miller's circumstances caused jealousy and occasionally led to millers being targeted during bread riots at times of famine. This arose from the system then prevalent whereby the Lord of the Manor exacted 'toll corn' from the peasants who were dependent upon the miller to produce supplies of flour for their own use. Usually between one-sixteenth and one twenty-fourth, it was an easy matter for the miller to set aside more than the agreed toll and keep the surplus for himself.

As late as the 1880s it was reported that Henry Liddington, the miller at Goldfield mill at Tring, was charged and convicted with taking excessive tolls. Frederick Eggleton, one of Liddington's customers, complained, and the matter went to court. A report in the *Herts Mercury* stated that . . . .

> ". . . . it appeared that Eggleton's wife and children had gleaned a quantity of wheat, which when thrashed weighed 232 lbs. This was taken to the defendant to grind, and when the flour was returned it only weighed 108 lbs. Allowing 14 lbs. per bushel waste, which was a fair amount, there was thus 60 lbs. short. Being dissatisfied, Eggleton went to the defendant and asked him for the offal, offering him at the same time 2s. for the grinding of the wheat. The defendant declined to give up the offal, and told Eggleton that he had received all the defendant intended he should have."

Found guilty, Henry Liddington was fined £10 plus costs. It is possible that he was the last windmiller in Hertfordshire, if not in England, to be convicted of this particular felony.

Food adulteration

Besides cheating on weight, a dishonest miller might also adulterate the flour. This was a more serious and potentially harmful matter but not uncommon throughout the food trade in bygone times. In *The Expedition of Henry Clinker* by Smollett (1771), a country squire comments thus on London's food . . . .

> *"The bread I eat in London is a deleterious paste, mixed up with chalk, alum and bone ashes: insipid to the taste and destructive to the constitution . . . the tallowy rancid mass called butter is manufactured with candle-grease and kitchen-stuff . . . ."*

An example reported in *The Northern Star* in 1846, describes how flour was adulterated with gypsum, a type of alabaster that could be ground to a fine white powder. The report states that a considerable quantity of gypsum was ground at a mill near Carlisle before being sent to Liverpool. It was then traced to William Pattinson of Cuddington Mill, near Weaverham, who was discovered by officers in the act of mixing it with flour. The newspaper ranted amusingly . . . .

> *"Thus is our 'daily bread' adulterated; thus is the craft of the mason carried on in our very stomachs, and mortar there produced which is of mortal effect; and thus a family wishing to purchase a stone of flour, is literally furnished with a flour of stone."*

For his crime Pattinson was fined £10 by Cheshire magistrates. Further down the production line the bakers were also at it using alum (potassium aluminium sulphate, or potash, which in large quantities is toxic) to bulk out flour while giving the bread a whiter colour and causing it to absorb and retain a larger amount of water than otherwise. This from the *Hampshire Telegraph* (1804) . . . .

"Near 50 bakers have been convicted at the different Police Offices within the last month, for selling bread deficient in weight. Many of them were likewise fined for having alum in their houses, with a view to mixing it with bread, a practice extremely prejudicial, particularly to infants."

Adulterating flour with alum remained a problem throughout the 19th century, as this extract from a manufacturing journal of 1880 illustrates . . . .

"However happy the effects of alum may be in improving the appearance of the bread and swelling the profits of miller and baker, the effects upon those who are obliged to eat such bread are liable to be most disastrous. . . . a very little alum in bread may not prove immediately or seriously injurious, but no considerable amount of such a powerful astringent is required to disorder digestion and ruin health, as is shown by a vast array of competent testimony."

But there were occasions when millers did tamper with the grain with good intention. This from a miller's handbook of 1881 . . . .

"A musty smell may be removed from grain by mixing powdered coal with it and letting it stand for fourteen

days, at the end of which time the coal dust is removed by the purifying machine. This treatment is said to remove every trace of mould, and the flour is excellent."

The reputation earned by millers endured to such an extent that surprise was registered when an honest miller was encountered, as is evidenced on a tablet in Great Gaddesden church, which reads . . . .

". . . . In memory of Thomas Cook, late of Noak Mill in this parish, who departed this life 8th December 1830, age 77. He was a good Husband and tender Father, and an honest man, although a miller."

The miller's trade

In giving their miller a reputation for greed and dishonesty, his contemporaries rarely appreciated that windmilling involved high fixed costs. The great millstones had to be dressed and set periodically, machinery broke down and windmills often suffered storm damage, which was expensive to repair, if indeed the storm had not brought about the mill's complete destruction. And to add to these risks and costs, windless periods would cause the mill, quite literally, to grind to a halt.

Millers who could not afford to maintain their millstones in the most efficient working order had to make do with a more precarious margin of profit. In his book *Wheat and the Flour Mill* (1920), Edward Bradfield, had this to say about the tedious but important process of dressing millstones . . .

". . . . half the miller's art - and it was an art - was comprised in laying out and dressing the stone. Properly to lay out a stone; to attain the absolute balance; to mark out the quarters, lands, and furrows and, finally, to give the requisite fineness of dress to the surface, required the skill and judgment, and steadiness of hand and eye, of no mean order, and the old stone millers rightly prided themselves on the quality of their work."

Figure 4.1 Two old millers. Mr J. B. Greater of Stratford St Andrew, Suffolk, and Mr J. Paris of Blackboys post mill, Framefield, East Sussex.

The millstones being set and dressed and the motive power being available - which for a windmill cannot be taken for granted - the process of milling can commence. The first task was to blend the various varieties of wheat to produce flour of the required character, then to rid the grain of impurities, such as stones, twigs, alien seeds and other extraneous matter that would adulterate the flour. This extract from an 1867 edition of *The Miller* magazine describes the process at that time . . . .

"The art of mealing, as it is called, consists in the judicious choice of wheat and in the proper arrangement of the machinery, so that the whole of the flour which the wheat is capable of producing may be obtained at one grinding.

The proper proportions of the wheat for grinding are mixed in a bin, after which the grain is passed through a blowing apparatus in order to separate dust and light particles. It is next passed through a smut machine, consisting of iron beaters enclosed within a skeleton cylindrical frame covered with wire, the spaces being wide enough to allow the impurities of the grain to fall through. The beaters revolve 400 or 500 times in a minute and by their action against the wires scrub the wheat, and remove portions of dust, smut, and impurities.

After this, the wheat is passed through a screen, arranged spirally on a horizontal axis, the revolutions of which scatter the seeds over the meshes, and allow small shrivelled seeds to pass through. The grain is next exposed to a current of air from a fan, which completes the removal of chaff, dirt, smutt-ball, etc.

The result of all this elaborate cleaning is greatly to improve the whiteness of the flour, and also its wholesomeness; and its necessity is evident from the accumulation of impure matter in the cases of the screens.

As the wheat passes from the last cleaning machine, it falls down a canvas tube into the hopper which supplies the millstones, where a jigging kind of motion is kept up, so as to shake the corn into the trough over the stones in equable quantities; and so long as this action is going on properly, a little bell is made to ring, the motion of which ceases with the supply of wheat."

This activity supposed that the wind was blowing sufficiently to drive the mill. Windless periods left the miller with a growing backlog of grain and no income, so when a windy period arrived it was usual for him to work day and night for several days on end to get as much done as possible while the wind lasted. It is unsurprising that even small country mills introduced small steam engines when these became available.

A tough business

As well as requiring great skill and experience, the miller's work was often arduous. Many worked ancient post mills fitted with simple sails, tail-poles, and manually-tentered stones. The miller had to be alert to any change in the wind; to an experienced miller's ear, the condition of the mill was evident from the sound of its machinery, while badly-adjusted stones could be detected from the smell of scorched meal ("nose to the grindstone").

Working old mills especially, could prove challenging when wrestling with wind and rain. When aware of a gathering storm, the miller had to apply the brake and reef the sails, a task that could take two men 30 minutes or more. Turning a post mill in a strong wind was also a slow job and could be an exhausting one. This was the experience of James Saunders, (1844-1935) who drove an old post mill at Stone near Aylesbury . . . .

> *"Many a time when I was out shifting the cloths in a storm* [reefing the sails], *the water has run off them down my arms and out of my trouser legs. Of course there was no chance of getting dry clothes until I went home, and in the winter they have sometimes been frozen onto me for hours . . . ."*

In more modern mills, self-reefing patent sails eliminated this arduous task.

Another aspect of milling that could, from time to time, make it a tough business was competition with other millers. Here Saunders reflects on a mill that he drove at High Wycombe . . .

> *". . . it was not a good neighbourhood and already overrun by millers. There were ten flour mills in the valley before we started; many of them paper mills converted into flour mills during the bad spell for paper-making, but all of them adding to the competition. Indeed when we began there was almost as many millers as bakers."*

And so in a buyers' market flour prices were driven down. This from the *Bucks Advertiser*, April 1876 . . . .

"Bucks County Lunatic Asylum.
To Millers –

Persons willing to supply FLOUR (about 9 sacks per week) as set forth in the printed forms of tender, for three months from the 18th day of March 1876 are requested to deliver at the Asylum at Stone, tenders on or before ten o–clock on the morning of Thursday the 16th instant . . . . Addressed to the Committee of visitors of the Bucks County Lunatic Asylum. A sample of flour will be shown at the Asylum; and a sample must be sent with the tender."

Another business risk that affected farmer and miller alike, was a poor wheat harvest. For several years James Saunders lived on the verge of bankruptcy, only surviving through the good offices of a sympathetic bank manager . . . .

"No country miller is likely to forget 1879, the worst year by far that I have ever known. The crop of English wheat was all bad alike, and country millers were entirely out of the market. Moreover, the competition of American flour became more severe; agents were travelling round practically everywhere offering it to every little village baker. Many mills were shut down at this time and never restarted again."

Dangerous work

Great care had also to be exercised in working a mill in an age when moving machinery was not always properly shielded, if

41

at all, from the unwary. This from the *Hampshire Telegraph* (1804) . . . . .

> *"A few days since, as John Ringer, aged 26, was attending a boulting* [sic] *mill* [it sifts meal into flour, etc], *in a windmill belonging to Mr. Francis Bacon, of Dickleburgh, the cogs caught hold of his frock smock, and so entangled him, that he was carried round by the same for three hours, in which time he was reduced to a most horrid spectacle."*

. . . . and from the *Caledonian Mercury* (1800) . . . .

> *"Yesterday evening the proprietor of the mill at Holyrood, had both legs most dreadful fractured, by the breaking of the millstone. Mr. Comins, the Staff Surgeon, being sent for, found the limbs in so shattered a state, that he was under the necessity of amputating both limbs immediately."*

For effective operation, windmills need a consistent draught with minimal turbulence from the surrounding landscape. Thus, they were often sited on isolated ground, but this left them more exposed to damage by storms and lightning strikes, problems made worse by their position generally being out of easy reach of water with which to fight fires. This from *The Standard* (1829) . . . .

> *"During the thunderstorm on Thursday, the windmill at Toot Hill, near Ongar, was struck with the lightning and literally dashed to pieces; parts of it were driven nearly 100 yards, and the corn strewed about; and a man*

The Miller and his mate making an inspection of the sails of the hundred years old windmill at Willesborough, Kent. Despite its age the mill is still capable of a steady output.

Figure 4.2 Millers climbing on the sails of Willesborough smock mill, Kent, 1938.

buried in the ruins has since been got out alive, but dreadfully bruised. The leg has been amputated . . . ."

. . . . two days later a further report of this incident appeared in *The Morning Chronicle*, embellishing the earlier details by informing readers that the victim was the miller . . . .

". . . . and his right hand mangled in a most frightful manner. . . . upon further examination, large splinters of wood, and even grains of wheat from the hopper, were found driven into various parts of his body."

This from the *Times* (1954) . . . .

"One of the last four working windmills in Lincolnshire, a county which at one time had over 400 in use, has been struck by lightning . . . the sails crashed through an adjacent engine house and were smashed to pieces . . . . and the foot thick shaft was snapped off when the lightning struck."

The absence of means to turn old post mills into the wind *automatically* made them particularly prone to storm damage. Indeed, both the post mills at Pitstone (*see Chapters 6 & 7*) were damaged beyond repair when struck from behind by sudden squalls before they could be winded, the outcome being chaos to their internal shafts and gearing before their sails were eventually torn from their windshafts. The vulnerability to storms of old windmills fitted with simple cloth sails, is illustrated in this experience of James Saunders while driving his post mill at Stone near Aylesbury . . . .

"A modern windmill is one thing, an antiquated post mill 400 years old, as mine was said to be, is quite another. . . . It was in October or November, at a time when I was so busy I had not kept a proper lookout for storms . . . and a tremendous hurricane caught me unawares. My first warning was that the mill was running faster and faster, but I was not really disturbed then until I had put the brake on and gone down to take some cloth off. Outside it was as black as pitch. I felt my way round to one sail and was just beginning to uncloth when the gale came on like mad. It blew me against the round-house, and away went the sails as if there was no brake on at all. I shall never forget how I rushed back up the ladder. The whole mill rocked so that the sacks of meal that were standing in the breast were thrown down like paper, but I got to the brake lever somehow and threw all my weight on it. I knew that if the brake were kept on she was bound to catch fire, so I let her off, and round she went, running at such a rate that the corn flew over the top and smoke blinded and suffocated me. . . . The sparks were flying out all round the brake as she groaned and creaked with the strain, but it still didn't stop the sails; and I doubt whether anything could, had not the hurricane itself subsided as suddenly as it sprung up."

And storms did cause mills that had 'run away' to catch fire; this from the *Morning Post* (1818) . . . .

"We this day give some further melancholy details of the effects of the late violent storm . . . at Exmouth, the violence of the gale carried round the vanes of the

*windmill with such velocity as to cause the works to take
fire, and the vanes were ultimately blown off, and dashed
to pieces."*

More substantially built tower mills fitted with fantails, and
thus less likely to be tail-winded, weathered storms better, but
when the sails were damaged, repairs could be very expensive.
To keep costs down, millers did what running repairs they
could themselves - particularly the lengthy task of dressing the
millstones - and only resorted to a millwright or the village
carpenter for specialist jobs.

Figures of speech: relics of the miller's trade

The millers of the past are not completely forgotten, although
few people realise this when they refer unknowingly to aspects
of the miller's trade, for certain of their idiomatic expressions
remain in common use today:

"Grind to a halt" refers to any process that will stop as a result
of a lack of materials or due to a breakdown in machinery. In a
mill, the millstones would literally "grind to a halt" if the wind
was not strong enough to drive them.

"Show one's metal/Show one's grit" is a figure of speech that
today has more to do with demonstrating courage than
experience, although it derives from the latter. When a miller
employed an itinerant stone dresser to resharpen his millstones,
the miller invited him to display his tools and his hands for the
miller's inspection to demonstrate his experience. The stone
dresser's tools are made of iron, and the back of the hands and
arms of an experienced stone dresser would be blackened by

the multitude of embedded fragments of metal and grit from the task of resurfacing the stones. Hence, to "show his metal".

"Rule of thumb" refers to the habit of the miller rubbing the flour between his thumb and forefinger to assess whether it was too coarse; if it was, he would reduce the gap between the grinding stones to produce finer flour.

"Grist to the mill" refers to a source of profit or advantage. Grist is the grain brought to a mill to be ground. In the days when farmers took grist to the mill the phrase would have been used to denote produce that was a source of profit.

"Keep your nose to the grindstone" means to apply yourself conscientiously to your work. This might have derived from the habit of millers, who checked that the stones used for grinding were not overheating, by putting their nose to the stone in order to smell any burning. But it is equally likely to have come from the knife-grinder's trade.

"Run-of-the-mill" - for a mill to produce flour of a consistent output, the grain had to be of a certain quality as had the milling process. Thus flour that met whatever criterion that had been set was described as run-of-the-mill, what we today might otherwise describe as "standard".

"A millstone around one's neck" is a Biblical metaphor meaning a burden or large inconvenience one has to endure.

"To be put, or to go through the mill" means to be exposed to hardship or rough treatment, just like grain being ground.

"Don't drown the miller" (little heard today) derives from the miller's once crucial position in rural society in the production of flour to make bread. This figure of speech was intended to convey the value of an asset (however unpopular, as the miller often was), for the obvious consequences of drowning the miller would be to deprive the community of a vital, possibly even life-sustaining, service. "Drowning" probably derived from watermills and their millponds being far more numerous than windmills.

APPENDIX I: wheat, flour and bread

Wheat flour is finely-ground grain. It is one of our most important foods, for it is the principal ingredient in most types of bread, biscuit and pastry.

Wheat probably developed from the accidental crossbreeding of certain grasses and by mutation. It was cultivated long before the beginning of recorded history, archaeologists having found evidence that it was grown in western Asia Minor at least 10,000 years ago. The ability to sow and reap cereals may be one of the reasons that led man to live in communities as opposed to following a wandering life hunting and herding animals. The Egyptians were to develop grain production along the fertile banks of the Nile and by about 3,000 BC they had evolved tougher varieties of wheat and had become skilful in baking bread.

Wheat grain needs to be crushed to extract the flour, but not all the grain is used. A grain of wheat (the *kernel*) has three main parts - *bran* is the tough outer covering; the embryo plant, or *germ*, is found in the bottom of the kernel; the remainder is the *endosperm*, a material composed largely of starch with some sugar. It is the endosperm alone that is used in the commercial mass-production of white flour.

The first task to perform before wheat can be ground into flour is to remove the heads from the top of the stalks. These are then *threshed*, a process that removes the edible grains from the rest of the head, called *chaff*. The grain is then ground to separate the bran, endosperm and germ. The resulting *meal* is sifted into various grades, white flour being the finest. White flour contains only the endosperm, while *wholemeal* flour contains all parts of the grain, which gives it a brownish appearance. Although wholemeal flour is more nourishing it suffers the disadvantages of a shorter shelf-life and, when used for baking, a poorer rising characteristic than white flour.

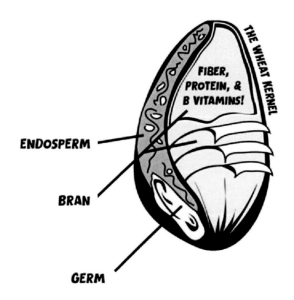

Figure 4.3 Milling essentially separates bran and germ from endosperm, reducing the endosperm to a uniform particle size (flour).

The earliest type of bread is believed to have been made from grains of wild grass, which were crushed by hand between two stones. The resulting meal was mixed with water to form dough, which was then baked on a stone over an open fire. This type of bread would have been very coarse and heavy in texture.

Yeast is known to have been used by the Egyptians in around 4,000 BC, first in brewing and then in baking. Perhaps wild yeast first drifted onto a dough that had been set aside before baking, causing it to rise enough to make the bread lighter and more appetizing than usual. This accidental process was then reproduced deliberately. But a more plausible theory is that, maybe by way of experiment, ale was used instead of water to mix the dough. The rise would have been greater than from wild yeast, and the effect would have been easier to explain and reproduce. The Egyptians also invented the closed oven and bread assumed great significance, being used instead of money; the workers who built the pyramids were paid in bread.

By 1,000 BC, leavened bread had become popular in Rome, and by 500 BC a circular stone wheel turning on top of another fixed stone was being used to grind grain; pairs of grindstones became the basis of all milling until the late 19th century and are still used today in the production of stone-ground flour. It is in this period that the waterwheel was invented by the Greeks and later adopted by the Romans who brought it to Britain.

During the Middle Ages, the growth of towns and cities saw a steady increase in trade and bakers began to set up in business, with bakers' guilds being introduced to protect their interests while controls also appeared to govern the price and weight of bread. By Tudor times, bread had become a status symbol, the nobility eating small white loaves, merchants and tradesmen wheaten cobs, while the poor ate bran loaves (the most nutritious).

During the 18th century sieves made of Chinese silk were introduced, which helped produce finer, whiter flour and white bread gradually became more widespread. Tin from Cornish mines was used to make baking tins resulting in bread (*tin loaves*) that could be sliced and toasted more easily and it was not long before the sandwich was invented. At this time and until well into the Victorian age bread was generally made from mixed grain; barley and rye breads took longer to digest and were favoured by labourers while the rich continued to eat the more expensive white wheat bread.

In the early 19th century, cheap imported wheat was becoming plentiful. To protect British grain prices and the income of the landed gentry, the Corn Laws of 1815 imposed a high import tariff on foreign-grown grain. The price of bread rose to as much as 2s.6d. a loaf, when some wages were only 3s. shillings a week. But despite the terrible suffering of the disenfranchised poor, the Corn Laws were not repealed until 1846.

The 19th century also saw the introduction of town gas, which replaced wood and coal to fuel bakers' ovens, producing much more even results, and the large automated baking units that followed increased bread production significantly.

Today, 76 per cent of the bread we eat is white, with sandwiches accounting for about half of this. Large bakeries producing wrapped and sliced bread (introduced here in the 1930s) account for 80 per cent of UK bread production, in-store bakeries produce about 17 per cent and the remainder is sold by high street bakeries.

Some traditional millers continue to use millstones, which unlike the steel rollers used to mill mass-produced flour, allows the miller to leave the whole grain intact, thereby adding a depth of flavour to the flour. Most commercial flour has the germ removed. Many independent bakers make a point of using stone-ground flours grown in Britain and milled at smaller-scale mills, for the resulting bread has more character and flavour. This is true of the bread produced in the small bakery attached to Redbournbury Water Mill, St. Albans (generally open to the public on Sunday afternoons).

APPENDIX II: gleaning

Gleaning is gathering grain left by the reapers. Some cultures promoted it as an early form of welfare system and in this context the Bible makes several references to gleaning, including Deuteronomy (24:19–21), which states the law thus . . . .

> *"When you are harvesting in your field and you overlook*
> *a sheaf, do not go back to get it. Leave it for the alien,*
> *the fatherless and the widow . . ."*

. . . which led to one poor biblical widow meeting her husband to be, for the romance between Ruth and the wealthy Boaz (Ruth 2) first sparked into life when Boaz caught sight of Ruth gleaning in his field after the reapers.

But gleaning did not always have a happy ending and until well into the 19th century it could lead to the prison cell. Under the heading A WOMAN IMPRISONED FOR GLEANING, the *Birmingham Daily Post*, 12th August 1868, carried a report of a *"poor woman"* imprisoned by Chester Magistrates. The newspaper informed its readers that a certain farmer had complained: *"I have had such a great deal of damage I want to make an example."* And an example their honours duly made; *"You must go to jail for seven days,"* was the verdict of the bench, but on sentence being passed one of the magistrates had second thoughts . . . .

> *"'I won't be a party to that. Seven days! All the papers in*
> *the country will be down us.'*

54

The defendant turned very pale, and, bursting into tears, said, 'Seven days for that! Don't send me to gaol from my four poor children, and one sucking at the breast.'"

Figure 4.4 Ruth gleaning, by Gustav Doré,
from the *Illustrated Bible* (1866).

Meanwhile the farmer was also back-tracking, for while he wished for some punishment *"he did not ask for so much as that"*. The commotion that followed caused their honours to reconsider, following which the sentence was reduced to a fine of 5s.6d. damages with 8s. costs (the wage of a farm labourer at that time was around 10s. a week); but as the defendant could not pay, she served three days in jail.

Despite the threat of jail, gleaning was commonplace, although subject to local rules as this extract from the *Farmer's Handbook* of 1814 describes . . . .

> *"The custom of gleaning is universal, and very ancient: in this country, however, the poor have no right to glean but by permission of the farmer; but the custom is old and so common, that it is scarcely ever broken through. It much behoves the farmer, in some places, where it is carried to excess, to make rules for the gleaners, and not to suffer them to be broken, under any pretence whatever."*

Each area of the country had its own customs, for instance at Gamnel Wharf mill in Tring, there was a day set aside to grind *'gleaners' corn'*, the cost of which was paid by keeping the bran, or, alternatively a quart out of a bushel of wheat. This old tradition worked well, except when the treatment of a gleaner was not scrupulously honest, as in the case of Frederick Eggleton and the miller of Goldfield described on page 33.

Gleaning remained an extremely important feature of rural life until the beginning of the 20th century, especially in times of agricultural depression when farm work was scarce. Many villagers relied on the flour that was derived from their autumn gatherings in the wheat fields to last the family throughout the year.

Chapter 5

THE MILLWRIGHT

The millwright's skills

The machinery on which the journeyman millwright worked is outlined in the two previous chapters. The following is a brief description of the skills exercised by these master craftsmen in designing, erecting and maintaining wind and water mills.

Figure 5.1 18th century millwrights at work.

The 19th century civil engineer, Sir William Fairbairn (1789-1874)[4] began his working life as an apprentice millwright at Newcastle-upon-Tyne. In his *Treatise on Mills and Millwork* (1865), Fairbairn provides an interesting insight into the millwright's work during the 18th century . . . .

---

[4] Fairbairn conceived the 'tubular bridge', first used to carry the Holyhead railway across the River Conway and the Menai Straits in North Wales.

*".... the millwright of the last century was an itinerant
engineer and mechanic of high reputation. He could
handle the axe, the hammer, and the plane with equal
skill and precision; he could turn, bore and forge with
the ease and despatch of one brought up to these trades,
and he could set out and cut in the furrows of a millstone
with an accuracy equal or superior to that of the miller
himself. These duties he was called upon to exercise, and
seldom in vain, as in the practice of his profession had
he mainly to depend upon his own resources."*

Thus, the millwright's trade combined elements of those of the
carpenter, blacksmith and stone mason, while he needed to be
of a practical and resourceful turn of mind. His occupation also
demanded the ability to *design* mills and milling machinery,
which required the application of arithmetic and geometry to
the manufacture of all the components of a working mill.
Fairbairn tells us that . . .

*".... he could calculate the velocities, strength, and
power of machines, could draw in plan, and section, and
could construct buildings, conduits, or watercourses, in
all the forms and under all the conditions required in his
professional practice. ...."*

During the windmill era, the millwright performed much of the
work of today's civil engineer and it is not difficult to see why
some of the more gifted among their ranks became our first
great civil engineers. Expertise also flowed in the opposite
direction. John Smeaton, famous for the Eddystone Lighthouse
(and the first to proclaim himself a *civil engineer*), while not a

Figure 5.2 Sir William Fairbairn, civil engineer (1789-1874)

millwright by trade, performed valuable research into the design of milling equipment. He investigated sail design and was the first to employ cast iron in place of wooden parts in the construction of milling machinery.

Fairbairn also tells us something about the millwright's standing in society . . . .

". . . . living in a more primitive state of society than ourselves, there probably never existed a more useful and independent class of men than the country millwrights. The whole mechanical knowledge of the country was centred amongst them, and, where sobriety was maintained and self-improvement aimed at, they were generally looked upon as men of superior attainments and of considerable intellectual power."

Perhaps Fairbairn's opinion was *rose-tinted*, for the two local millwrights for whom we have been able to obtain information, while offering the range of skills that he describes, do not appear to have matched them with a high degree of business acumen.

Local millwrights

The Hillsdons of Tring

Waddesdon-born John Hillsdon came to Tring in about 1825. The 1841 Census records him living at Tring Wharf with his wife and five children, where he worked as a miller at Gamnel Wharf mill (*Chapter 8*) together with his 16-year old son, John.

By 1850 John had left Gamnel to trade on his own account, describing himself as a 'Millwright' and occupying premises on the corner of Chapel Street and King Street in Tring. Ten years later the Hillsdon's venture into the world of business had proved unwise, for their financial affairs were in a parlous condition. On 15th December 1860 an announcement appeared on the front page of *The Bucks Advertiser & Aylesbury News:*

> *"Notice is hereby given that by indenture dated the 7th day of December 1860, John Hillsdon the elder and John Hillsdon the younger of Tring, in the County of Hertford, Engineers, assigned all their personal estate and effects whatsoever and wheresoever to William Smith Simkin of No 6 Leadenhall Street, London, Ironmonger, and John Nevins of Nos 1 & 2 Great Guildford Street, London, Ironmonger, upon Trust for the benefit of themselves, and all the creditors of the said John Hillsdon the elder and John Hillsdon the younger . . . . In the presence of John Merritt Shugar of Tring, Solicitor."*

In spite of this drastic measure, the following year Johns senior and junior - now described as agricultural machine makers - are found in the records of the Hertford Union Gaol & House of

Correction, imprisoned for debt. By no means an uncommon offence at that time, the Hillsdon's fellow inmates were other assorted traders, including a china dealer, a market gardener and a straw hat maker.

How long the pair remained incarcerated is not known but they weathered this setback and returned to carry on business in the same premises as before. In 1869 John junior placed an ambitious advertisement for Tring Iron Works in *Kelly's Trade Directory,* where he is described as *"engineer; millwright; manufacturer of portable and fixed steam engines, water wheels; corn, bone, bark and colour miller; and iron and brass founder".* No more is heard of John junior in Tring, but it is thought that he and wife emigrated to New Zealand, leaving there seven years later for the USA. However, George, a younger son, also followed the family tradition and remained with his father at the King Street business.

It is recorded that the firm of Hillsdon erected the tower mill at Hawridge Common *(see Chapter 10),* and installed the steam engine at Wendover windmill *(see Chaper 11),* but apparently John senior never made his fortune for his last record is in 1871, a widower of 76 living in lodgings in Frogmore Street, Tring. It is believed that the Hillsdon's firm, Tring Ironworks, closed around 1905.

William Cooper of Aylesbury

Almost all that is known of William Cooper and his business are contained in two account books now held in the Buckinghamshire Archives.

On October 11th, 1831, an announcement in the *London Gazette* stated that the partnership between William and Joseph Cooper, Millwrights and Smiths of Aylesbury, Bucks, had been dissolved by mutual consent. The following year William Cooper was declared bankrupt, his two account books passing into the custody of the court. One is a general ledger in which are recorded his business transactions between May 1827 and September 1832, the other records expenses incurred between April 1830 and January 1831 in connection with fitting out Champness windmill at Fulmer.

In common with the Hillsdons, the ledger shows that Cooper performed a surprising range of work. This extended from simple repairs to stoves and locks, to more complex work on agricultural machinery, through to the installation of all the equipment at Fulmer and Quainton (*Chapter 13*) windmills. The ledger also shows that Cooper worked on some thirty wind and water mills in and around Aylesbury, including a windmill at Tring (but unclear which mill - *Chapters 8 & 9*) and those at Waddesdon (*Chapter 6*), Wingrave (*Chapter 6*), and Wendover (*Chapter 11*). He also undertook work on the treadmill in Aylesbury Gaol and on an unspecified type of mill at Winslow Workhouse.

The cost of fitting out Champness mill was £445.8s.10d., of which almost half was for labour, the balance being for canvas (121 yards), tacks (22,000), screws (13 gross), nails, chisels, ironwork, timber, and *"Different things"*. Wages paid to the skilled men were four shillings a day, while the daily rate for the two labourers was two shillings.

Among Cooper's smaller jobs are recorded the repair of butter churns; roughing of horse shoes; mending wagons; repairing a kitchen range; mending a rat trap; ringing pigs; mending plough shears; and to a Mr. Collins he supplied *"12 stoves different sizes"*. If nothing else it seems that the millwright of the age was versatile.

What led to Cooper's bankruptcy is unknown, although in the Fulmer book there are references to expenses of a legal nature: *"Copy of a Rit"* (writ)*,* expenses for *"Sherrfs officer"*, and *"Lawyer Charge"*, which suggest that he might have been owed money for work on the mill. There are several entries referring to the purchase of pints and quarts of gin and rum.

Apart from these account books, the Aylesbury Poor Rate Book for 1831-2 records that Cooper's premises were in Walton Street on a site now occupied by the *White Swan*, but by 1835 the foundry had gone.

Decline of the millwright's trade

As the Industrial Revolution progressed, millwrights were pressed into service to build the first powered textile mills. James Watt's condensing steam engine developed into an economical and reliable driving force and, unlike wind and water power, one that offered a stable source of motive power. Gradually, wind and water mills were replaced, first by steam-driven machinery and eventually by electric power, while small local grain mills gave way to large factory units catering for entire regions of the country. As for the millwright, his work was lost in the evolution of other trades, such as turners, fitters, machine makers and mechanical engineers.

Chapter 6

VANISHED WINDMILLS AROUND TRING

What's in a name?

This chapter describes the evidence for windmills that once existed in the locality of Tring but about which little is now known.

Once a windmill is demolished and the physical evidence of it disappears, it soon becomes difficult to piece together its history from what documentary evidence remains in local trade directories of the period, in parish histories and in old letters, books, maps and pictures. Place names, such as Windmill Field or Hill, Windmill Lane or Road, Windmill Farm, etc., sometimes offer a clue to location, for what they now represent was very likely at, or near to, the site of a windmill. Take for example the plot of land in central London that came into the possession of one Thomas Wilson, a brewer, in June 1561. He built a windmill on the site, hence the name of 'Great Windmill Street' in Piccadilly (*Survey of London*, Vol. 31 & 32).

Tring

From the time of Domesday until the middle of the 16th century, streams in and around Tring drove three different watermills; so it can be assumed that in medieval times there was no need to erect any windmills. When these watermills fell into disuse is not known but, then as now, technology changed and the first windmill symbol for Tring appeared in 1766 on a map surveyed by the famous cartographers, Andrews and Drury.

Figure 6.1 A mill symbol, *c.*1766, is in the centre of the map, just below 'New Mill' on the south side of Icknield Way.

The windmill depicted on this map (*fig. 6.1*) was sited three quarters of a mile north of the parish church, on the Icknield Way, half way between the cross roads at the top of what is now Dundale Road and New Mill. A windmill is also shown in this position on the Inclosure map of 1797; valued by the Commissioners at 6s.2d., it is listed as belonging to Edward Foster's Trustees. However, the exact site is a puzzle for on a map of 1822 surveyed by Andrew Bryant, the windmill symbol appears at the junction of Dundale Road and Icknield Way. Whether one or other of the map-makers made an error and wrongly positioned the mill, or it was moved, is not known.

Figure 6.2 A post mill mounted on a sledge being moved by 86 oxen. This mill, near Brighton, was in 1797 moved for a distance of 2 miles.

Although uncommon, windmills were moved occasionally, as this account of the procedure for bodily removing a post mill illustrates . . . .

"If the main post and crosstrees were to be retained, they might be removed complete with the mill carcass; the crosstrees (fig. 2.2) would be shored up, brick piers demolished, and the trolley run underneath the structure, which was then let down bit by bit with jacks and levers. Sometimes in Suffolk two 'drogues' (or timber wagons) were lashed together side-by-side, two arms of the crosstrees being rested on one, and two on the other . . ."

66

. . . . and many horses or oxen were then teamed to haul the resulting load.

In any case, no other records of Tring's old windmill on Icknield Way are mentioned in any local records. The late Bob Grace, who owned Grace's Maltings in Akeman Street, claimed that a 3ft 'Cullin Stone' (a name given by millers to black millstones imported from the Cologne area of Germany) from this old post mill was set into the courtyard of his premises.

Aldbury

In *Aldbury the Open Village,* (pub. 1987), Jean Davis, the Aldbury historian, writes that . . . .

> *"in the southwest corner of Aldbury Parish, Great and Little Windmill Fields recall the mill which would have served Pendley Manor, but as early as 1354 it was in very bad condition."*

Two maps of Aldbury, one dated 1762 and the other 1803, show a Great Windmill Field and a Little Windmill Field in an area about one and a quarter miles south-west of the church. These fields are near both the Tring and Wigginton parish boundaries with Aldbury and an account of the bounds of Tring Manor in 1650 contains what seems to be a reference to this windmill site. . . .

> *". . . . and soe a longe the highway between Aldbury ffield and Tringe ffield and soe to Pendley Lockshops*

*and from thence unto Pendley gate and from thence to
Windmill Corner and from thence to old well . . . ."*

These references to known landmarks locate Windmill Corner
as adjacent to the Windmill Fields.

Even more mystery surrounds the second windmill in Aldbury.
A rental document, with an approximate date of 1501,
mentions a "wynd Milfelde", the site being about two-thirds of
a mile west-north-west of the church. Further evidence of a
windmill in this position comes from a map of the Duke of
Bridgewater's estate dated 1762 which names a Windmill Hill.
On an aerial photograph of 1972, there is a circular crop mark
in the position where it is thought to have been sited.

A further shred of evidence can be found in the *Victoria
County History of Hertford* (Vol.2), which states that a
windmill was erected in Aldbury towards the end of the 16th
century. In 1589-90, a licence was asked for by Thomas Kynge
to erect a cottage for the miller *"a painfull man in his calling".*
This latter does not quite agree with the other dates, but in
discussing matters so long ago, a difference of one hundred
years has sometimes to be expected; all that is certain is that
there has been no working windmill at Aldbury for a very long
time.

Pitstone's mystery mill

The post mill at Pitstone (*Chapter 7*), now in the care of the
National Trust, is well known and documented. What is less
known - indeed, almost unknown - is that it once had a near

neighbour, another post mill, which was located on land that is now developing into the Castle Mead estate.

Although there is still local recollection of this nameless mill being talked about, the sole documentary evidence for it lies in an account written during the 1930s by Stanley Freese, a well-known writer on windmills. Freese admits that the mill is not shown on standard maps of the period, *"although the early 6in and 25in O.S. outlined the mill mound without naming it"*. However, local historians at Pitstone Green Museum were able to locate the mill on an undated tithe map, standing adjacent to the course of the former Marsworth to Pitstone Road.

Figure 6.3 The long vanished post mills at Bledlow Ridge and at Long Crendon, photographed *c.*1930.

Freese's single type-written sheet gives a brief account of an interview that he had with one John Tompkins, whose family drove the mill. Tomkins told Freese that his father *"had the mill until about 1861"* when he left for America and that the mill met its demise shortly afterwards. In Freese's words. . . .

> *"Mr. Tompkins believes that the late Mr. Hawkins, who eventually had Ivinghoe Mill* [the National Trust mill], *took the old one from his father, but in any case it would have been only for a year or two; for the mill 'ran away' in a gale whilst the miller and an old man named Corkett were in it; and before it could be checked two of the sails were hurled from the mill. The miller anticipated the catastrophe and shouted to Corkett to look out, but the latter being very deaf did not hear the miller's shout above the gale; and found the roundhouse, in which he was at work, falling about him, and a sail coming through the roof. He escaped serious injury however."*

Such were the risks of windmilling, and it is coincidental that Pitstone windmill met with a similar catastrophe in 1902.

The mystery mill must have been badly damaged, for it was demolished shortly afterwards. John Hawkins, a local farmer interviewed by Freese, had known old Corkett and although he did not recall the mill he did remember that its brick piers remained for a time before they, the mound on which the mill stood and its access path (which lay adjacent to the old *Ship Inn* in Vicarage Road) disappeared under the plough.

The description given to Freese was of a post and roundhouse structure of average size, but not as big as Pitstone Mill, nondescript in colour, with four cloth sails and a tail post and wheel. It was equipped with both wheat and barley stones, side by side, but it is thought not to have been a flour mill but employed in grinding animal feed. The mill is believed to have belonged to the Ashridge Estate and Freese thought it possible that the Estate later purchased Pitstone Mill to replace it.

Cholesbury

Yet another mystery windmill was sited on the east side of Cholesbury Common. This is shown on Robert Morden's 1695 map of Buckinghamshire and also that of his copyist Emanuel Bowen's map of 1760. About a furlong south of Tring Grange Farm, the position marked is now just over the Hertfordshire border. According to local tradition, the exact site was not actually Windmill Field, which would place it on a hillside, but in the next field upon the hilltop. However, at the time of writing it remains a mystery, for no remains have been discovered.

Hawridge Common

In the words of Stanley Freese, a *"fine-looking though not well designed smock mill"* (*fig. 6.4*) was erected on Hawridge Common by the Norwich Wind and Steam Mill Company in 1863, and came complete with steam engine to supplement the wind; old photographs depict an impressive brick chimney and, by 1866, a delivery note for half a sack of flour (at 18s.0d.) was headed "Hawridge Wind and Steam Mill". The chimney was pulled down in 1884 (*fig. 10.6*).

As far as Buckinghamshire is concerned, Hawridge smock mill was unusual in having a square brick base of two storeys, above which was a narrow wooden tower whose walls were

71

tarred. The four white sweeps were of the patent anti-clock double-shuttered type, and the fantail was six-vaned.

Figure 6.4 Hawridge smock and steam mill.

There is no continuous and completely reliable record of the various millers and owners of Hawridge. Millers who can be traced through the census returns are . . . .

1861 Thomas Moreton, miller, born Nuneaton
Charles Pedel, journeyman miller, born Wendover

1871 Joseph Salt, miller, born Congleton
George Salt, miller, born Warwickshire
George Wright, miller, born Cholesbury

1877 William Wright, miller

1881 Harry Wright, miller, born Tring

Original documents show that the mill was acquired in 1871 by Humphrey Dwight, described as a pheasant breeder from Wigginton, who purchased it from a consortium at Great Windsor. He paid £700, which included "*a messuage, granary and premises*", the legal aspects of the sale being handled by Smith, Fawdon & Low of Chesham and Shugar, Vaisey & Co. of Tring.

It seems that Dwight did not prosper, for ten years later the freehold again changed hands. Dwight (described in the 1881 Census as a farmer of 140 acres employing 5 labourers, and resident at 24 Bellingdon Road, Chesham) called again on the services of Tring solicitor, Arthur Vaisey, who prepared on his behalf the following statement dated 14th February 1881 . . . .

"I the undersigned Humphrey Dwight of Bellingdon near Tring having been served with a Writ for the sum of £578.5s.2d. due from me for principal and interest to the executors of the late Mr John Merritt Shugar which sum is charged upon my freehold mill and premises situate at Hawridge Bucks hereby authorise and request you to take the necessary steps on my behalf for selling the said mill and premises either by public auction or private

contract and also to endeavour to get any further proceedings on the said Writ stayed pending the sale of the property."

On 26th February, William Brown & Co. received instructions to auction the mill, the sale being held at the *Rose and Crown Inn*, Tring. The auctioneers described the property as a . . . .

"Free hold Windmill with steam power attached, driving four pairs of stones, situate on Cholesbury Common, part in the Parish of Cholesbury, part in the Parish of Hawridge; also capital residence with garden, yard, and stabling. The property is in the occupation of Mr Wright, a yearly tenant at a rent of £400 p.a."

The sale realised exactly £600, which Humphrey Dwight was obliged to surrender to settle the debt together with a further £20.18s.5d. to cover auctioneer's and solicitor's fees.

The mill is believed to have been bought by another member of the extensive Dwight dynasty, Daniel, who, at some time between 1881 and 1883 demolished it and built the tower mill (*Chapter 10*) that stands today. The reasons for demolishing a mill only twenty years old were given as inconvenient arrangement; poor construction; loading floor on the ground instead of at cart-level; and no bin floor, resulting in grain having to be fed directly into the eye of the millstones instead of being shot down from storage bins in the floor above. These defects probably rendered the mill unprofitable to work, and might in turn explain the frequent change of millers. But one miller is known to have given up the mill for an unrelated reason. Joseph Salt met a tragic death when, helping to right a derailed locomotive in the neighbouring Tring valley, he failed to let go of a lever when it was released by the other workmen, and was killed as a result.

During its demolition, the smock mill's machinery and other parts were salvaged to be incorporated in the new tower mill. Today, a fitting reminder of Hawridge's old smock mill lives on in the shape of the logo of the Hawridge & Cholesbury Cricket Club, whose members are fortunate enough to have a pitch on the beautiful Common.

Marsworth

The Domesday survey records three mills in the Manor of Marsworth. By 1292 a water mill existed, valued at £4.9s.4d., which descended through various owners, eventually becoming known locally as Dyer's Mill. It stood in the south-west corner of the village, and according to the *Victoria County History* (Vol.3), it was "turned into a windmill", which seems quite possible since the construction of the Grand Junction Canal diverted the water, thereby incapacitating all Marsworth's watermills.

A reference of 1817 records that a Thomas Sear insured a brick and timber wind-driven corn mill with no kiln and two pairs of stones for £600 and an adjoining house for £200, the whole a quarter of a mile west-south-west of Marsworth church. In 1824, members of the Sear family leased the premises to William Pickett, shopkeeper of Marsworth. These included "*a recently erected windmill on the same site of the former watermill*".

Twenty years later Thomas Sear sold the mill to a horse dealer, Charles Gregory, who took over the £400 mortgage. After a few years it was sold on again to Thomas Clarke, miller of Tring, who in his turn took over the mortgage and insurance payments, also obtaining a second mortgage of £1,000 to erect a steam mill *"adjoining to the said Wind Corn Mill"*. The Indenture included a requirement to keep *"the wind corn mill insured against loss or damage by fire, and to run the business correctly"*. By 1875 the mortgage was paid off.

Thomas Clarke died intestate, and his property was offered for sale at the *Rose & Crown*, Tring; Thomas Mead, a local miller, bought the entire premises for £1,500. According to the sale advertisement that appeared in the *Bucks Advertiser* during January, 1881, it comprised . . . .

> *". . . . a Steam Mill of 5 floors fitted with a 12 hp. Steam Engine, a 16 hp boiler, 3 pairs of stones with elevators, and all necessary shafting and gearing, most completely fitted, and all in perfect order; a SIDE MILL of 4 floors, communicating therewith from each floor; a bean and drying kiln; a comfortable dwelling house, adapted for the proprietor with all necessary fittings; a stable for 4 horses, with loft over; various convenient out-houses; good garden; close of pasture and orchard land, together about one acre, one rood, and one pole, upon which a lucrative business has for 28 years past been carried out . . . . "*

Thomas Mead already owned a new steam-driven mill at Gamnel Wharf, Tring, and bought Marsworth windmill possibly as a strategic purchase to prevent any competition with this new venture. However, he had no use for the old windmill which was eventually demolished *c*.1919.

Elderly residents of Marsworth, when interviewed during the 1930s, recalled that the windmill's sails were torn off in a gale in about 1845 and the gear so damaged that for a considerable time the mill was unworkable. A man who assisted with the demolition remembered it being built of red brick, four storeys high but without a stage, and with four patent sweeps and the usual fantail.

Other vanished windmills

In his book *Hertfordshire Windmills and Windmillers*, Cyril Moore refers to several windmills in the locality of Tring about which little is known. That at Abbots Langley, believed to have been in the vicinity of Catsdell Bottom, was standing in 1912 in a derelict condition. There is evidence of two windmills at Berkhamsted, one of which, a post mill, is depicted in an 18th century view of the town that places it in the vicinity of Millfield Road. The windmill at Little Gaddesden probably disappeared in antiquity, with old references to a "Mill Field" to the south-east of the church being its last trace.

To the north of Tring, there were windmills at, among other places, Brill (other than the post mill that still stands), Wing, Wingrave and Waddesdon.

There is no record of when Waddesdon mill was built, although it was standing in 1834, for in Cook's *History of the English Turf* the author describes a steeplechase run in that year over a course from Waddesdon windmill to Aylesbury

Figure 6.5 Waddesdon mill.

Church, while from a slightly earlier period the account book of the Aylesbury millwright William Cooper (*Chapter 5*) records that he undertook work on a windmill at "Wadsdon". The mill is said to have been a particular favourite of Miss Alice de Rothschild, who had inherited the great Waddesdon estate from her brother, Baron Ferdinand. In its latter day this attractive tile-hung windmill was said to be more ornamental than practical, for local rumour has it that if the wind was favourable it was set to work for no better purpose than to greet Miss Alice on her return to the village after her absences abroad, and she is believed to have paid for its restoration in the early years of the 20th century (c. 1905). *English Windmills* (Vol. 2) records that (c. 1930) the mill was "*slowly decaying*"; according to Stanley Freese, it met its fate when "*it was dynamited by the Baron's nephew for no apparent reason in the summer of 1932*".

Wing's windmill is marked on the 1770 and 1788 Thomas Jeffery maps of Buckinghamshire situated on the northern side of Aylesbury Road. The windmill had ceased operations by

1798 when it was noted as "due to be taken down immediately" in the Posse Comitatus[5] of that year.

Figure 6.6 Post mills at Brill.

The mill in the foreground is that which stands today. In the background can be seen Parson's Mill, built in 1634. It was struck by lightning in 1905 - a common fate for windmills - and demolished the following year.

The smock mill at Wingrave stood at Windmill Farm. It had been moved from Whitchurch in 1809 and operated at Wingrave until about 1872, when it was replaced by a steam mill elsewhere in the village. In December, 1841, the *Aylesbury News* announced that . . . .

---

[5] A register of all able bodied men, not already serving in a military capacity, between the ages of 15 and 60. It also recorded details about mills.

"Wingrave Windmill - the above mill having undergone extensive repairs and improvements W. Burton begs to inform his friends that he will work day and night (wind permitting) to fetch up his arrears of grinding".

The windmill's sails evidently came very near to the ground, for it is recorded that they once killed a passing pig.

At Wendover, a windmill is marked on maps by Jefferys (1768) and by Andrews and Drury (1809) standing upon the high ground adjoining Hale Road and almost opposite the east end of Chapel Lane, about a quarter of a mile north-east of the Parish Church. The name of the field where the mill stood is Snail Hill, but nothing else is known about it.

These are just a few of the windmills that once graced our locality and that gradually fell into disuse and decay as industrialisation progressed and our way of life changed. An article in the *Home Counties Magazine* (Vol. II., 1900) gives a contemporary view of these romantic, but sadly vanishing landmarks . . . . .

"With the increasing application of steam to milling purposes, and the improved means of transport of foreign flour, it is pretty clear that the days of windmills, if not quite over, are rapidly becoming fewer, and at no very distant date most of the numerous picturesque examples now left in the Home Counties will have fallen victims to neglect and decay, or have been swept away to make room for more utilitarian buildings. . . . the old windmill on Mitcham Common is likely to disappear

before long. For so many years it has been one of the chief landmarks of the Mitcham district, and especially of the heath upon which it stands, that its removal can hardly fail to produce that feeling of regret which is inseparable from the destruction of old and familiar features in a landscape."

Where a windmill has left any trace at all, it is often in nothing more than a name, the significance of which has long been forgotten.

Chapter 7

PITSTONE MILL

Figure 7.1 Hand reaping in Windmill Field, Pitstone.

Despite its inanimate nature, Pitstone post mill always appears to be lonely, particularly so when viewed from a distance in silhouette, its upper sweeps outstretched like two skeletal arms pointing accusingly at the sky. And well they might, for a sudden gale caught the miller unawares and, before he could wind the mill, almost destroyed it. Thanks to its donor, Leonard Hawkins and to the band of brothers who toiled for many years over its resurrection, Pitstone windmill continues to stand, a lonely sentinel over the bare expanse of Windmill Field.

The village of Pitstone derives its name from the Anglo Saxon for 'Picel's thorn tree'; it appears in the Domesday Book (1086) as 'Pincelestorne', a holding of William the Conqueror's half-brother, the Count of Mortain, who also held land in nearby Tring. Although not listed in Domesday, a watermill probably existed in Pitstone as a necessity to village life, but it was not until 1231 that the first watermill is recorded. Further references appear in 14th, 16th and 17th century documents, the mill referred to latterly probably being that which still exists at Ford End and which is opened to the public.

The Domesday Survey predates the coming of the windmill to Britain by a century or more. If a windmill did exist at Pitstone during the medieval period, there is no record of it. The first mention of a windmill arises in records held in the Bucks Record Office for the years 1624 to 1628. These refer to the tenants of the 'Windmill at Ivinghoe' and to payments made to carpenters working on its structure. They further suggest it to be an old mill at the time. Archaeological evidence of its age exists in the date '1627' carved into one of its internal timbers, while dendrochronology suggests a date of 1590. Neither can be relied upon, for the timbers could well have been recycled from an earlier building. Whatever the mill's exact date-of-birth, there is sufficient evidence to place it at least in the early 17th century, making it one of the oldest remaining windmills in Britain, possibly *the* oldest.

In his historical note on nearby Brook End watermill, Keith Russell, the present owner, has this to say about the close relationship of Pitstone's three mills . . . .

"Pitstone Windmill (dated 1627) has always been linked with Pitstone Mill. The two were connected by a 'good road' then known as the Mill Way, and it followed the line of what is Orchard Way. The Whistle Brook, also known as the Missel Brook because of the propensity of fresh water mussels therein, was the source of power. Often in the past the Windmill, Pitstone Watermill and Ford End Watermill have been worked simultaneously by the same individual, which is not surprising when you realize that as the crow flies they are all just a short walk away from each other."

The earliest person known to be connected with Pitstone mill was John Burt, who in 1770 occupied The Mill House (Brook End) and owned both wind and watermills. These he bequeathed to his son James in 1786. Two years later James insured both mills and other premises with The Sun Fire Insurance Company for the sum of £400; in 1801 he switched to the Royal Exchange Fire Insurance Company, the cover for the windmill stating . . . .

"On his Corn Windmill house, timber built, situate at a distance from the above [i.e. Brook End mill house] £50. On the standing and going gears, millstones, machines, etc. therein £50. Warranted no steam engine in either mill."

The caveat is interesting, not so much because steam engines were regarded as an increased fire risk, but the suggestion is that at this early date they were already being used in mills to supplement wind and water power.

James sold both mills at auction at the *Rose and Crown Inn* at Tring in 1810, the windmill being advertised as . . . .

"a capital and substantially built Wind Corn Mill, standing in the open field of Pitstone about two furlongs from the house, on an excellent site, and a good road; the whole admirably calculated for a mealman, being situate in a good corn country where mills are scarce. Land tax £1-3-4d. per annum."

The buyer was probably the Grand Junction Canal Company (the company was to sell both mills in 1842) who might have wished to gain control of the ground water in the area.

Pitstone windmill's next recorded miller was Benjamin Anstee, who is listed in *Pigot's Directory* for 1823 and whose surname was also carved on the old mill door. The windmill again changed hands in 1842, when Francis Beesley bought it from the Grand Junction Canal Company,[6] retaining the mill until 1874 when it was bought by the 3rd Earl Brownlow, owner of the Ashridge Estate. The windmill was later let to the Hawkins family, tenants of the surrounding Pitstone Green Farm. John Hawkins employed a miller named Jim Horn, who is believed to have worked the mill until around 1894, to be followed by Charles Simmons, the last recorded miller. Following the death of the 3rd Earl and the break-up of the Ashridge Estate, the Hawkins family bought the farm and windmill in 1924.

The body of the mill was renovated in 1894, which included re-boarding. The author Stanley Freese, writing in the 1930s,

---

[6] Auctioned by Messrs Gibbs and Sons, the *King's Head Inn*, Ivinghoe, 6th June 1842 (*Bucks Advertiser and Aylesbury News*, 14th May, 1842).

states that the job was carried out by a workman named John Payne, "*said to have been exceptionally clever with his tools, being able to do inlaid work amongst other things*". The work being completed at Christmas, Payne then "*got on to the top ridge of the body and walked along it in his bare feet to fix a sprig of holly on the tail*". The mill's post and trestle were open to the weather until the roundhouse was built shortly after the renovation work was completed, for it bears the date 1895 upon a cement slab low down on the outer wall. Freese records that it was of yellow brick (it is now whitewashed) and had four doorways, but the doors and frames were never fitted.

In 1902 the mill's working life came to an abrupt end:

> "*a great gale rose and caught the mill tail-winded, thrusting the sails forward, lifting the tail of the windshaft out of its seating, and finally blowing two sails off altogether.*"

The damage was such as to place it beyond economic repair and over the following decades Pitstone mill fell into progressive decay. In *English Windmills* Vol. II (1932) the mill's plight is described thus . . . .

> "*This is a post mill standing alone in the middle of a very large field, on the road from Ivinghoe to Pitstone. It is derelict. The roundhouse of yellow brick was a comparatively recent addition and is now covered with corrugated iron. The trestle timbers have some good moulding, but had apparently weathered a good deal before the addition of the roundhouse. . . . It has now no ladder, tail pole or sails. There are remnants of*

machinery still in position and two large millstones on the floor. It should be emphasised that such a building is not safe in any way, and that visitors can see all that need be seen from without."

Figure 7.2 Pitstone mill *c*.1930.

At some time during the 1930s, Stanley Freese wrote an interesting account of Pitstone mill based on his observations and on interviews with people he does not name, but possibly members of the Hawkins family. In Freese's view, the mill had sufficient similarity to that at Brill to suggest that Pitstone was the product of the same millwright. He goes on to describe the mill in considerable detail, also giving some idea of the miller's everyday activities . . . .

"Two pairs of stones, 3ft 10in and 4ft, are placed side by side upon the upper floor. . . . in a good east wind both pairs of stones could be worked, but this entailed a lot of rushing about the mill; one pair could often be worked with two sails half-clothed and the other two furled. . . . When worked ceased, the sweeps were always placed on the cross, so that the tips were out of reach of mischief makers who might otherwise climb up the bottom sail and get into the trap door in the breast of the mill over

the windshaft neck. This extremely unusual door . . . was provided for the purpose of greasing the neck bearing . . . . and in milling days this neck was greased every morning before starting work."

It was not until 1937 that the resurrection of Pitstone mill began. Its then owner, Leonard Hawkins (*fig. 7.3*), dismayed by its sad condition and his inability to restore it, gave the derelict hulk to the National Trust together with access rights across his land. Shortage of funds meant that little could be done other than to make cosmetic repairs[7] and stabilise the mill's structure to prevent further deterioration, although work on the roundhouse that had begun in 1895, was completed, two of its four doorways being bricked up. In 1938, Freese records that the fourth was *"provided with a beautiful iron-studded oak door the like of which has probably seldom been seen on a windmill."*

Figure 7.3 Leonard Hawkins, c. 1905

Other than necessary remedial work to stem the ravages of time, no further restoration took place until 1963 when the

---

[7] Repairs were undertaken by the Tring boat-building firm of Bushell Bros.

Figure 7.4 The restoration of Pitstone mill.

Pitstone Windmill Restoration Committee was formed and a plan drawn up to restore the windmill to full working order by voluntary effort. A survey of the structure showed that, although much needed to be done, it was in better condition than had been feared. Donations from various sources raised £1,000 towards the restoration, materials were given free or at a discount, equipment was lent, and the carpentry students at Aylesbury College made the mill's sails. After much voluntary effort, Pitstone mill again ground grain in 1970.

Pitstone mill is now maintained (as a non-working exhibit) by the National Trust.

Chapter 8

GAMNEL WHARF MILL (NEW MILL)

Figure 8.1 Gamnel Wharf Flour Mills, seen from the Wendover Arm.

Heygates Mill, the large flour mill that stands in Tringford Road adjacent to the Wendover Arm of the Grand Union Canal, was once the site of Gamnel Wharf [8] windmill. Although this chapter is concerned principally with the history of the windmill, it also includes a brief account of the present flour mill, which supplies flour to customers over a wide area of southern England and is a significant employer in the town.

The new canal and Gamnel Wharf

An early outcome of the Industrial Revolution was the building of our canal network, which was to improve so dramatically the transport of goods, particularly those in bulk such as coal and grain. Many local businessmen and farmers soon became aware of the great potential that this new form of transportation could have on their profits, and factories, wharfs and mills of different types soon sprung up along the banks of the new waterways.

The Grand Junction Canal, as it was then named, reached West Hertfordshire towards the end of the 18th century, winding its way through the meadows and sleepy towns of the locality, but bypassing Tring. However, the need to provide the canal with a sufficient water supply as it crossed its summit in the Chiltern Hills led to the construction of a small feeder canal, the Wendover Arm. This spur, which opened in 1797, ran westwards along a contour of the Chilterns, tapping into local brooks and reservoirs along its route; and the Wendover Arm *did* pass the outskirts of Tring, at Gamnel. Originally intended

---

[8] . . . . also known as 'Tring Wharf'.

as nothing more than a feeder, the Arm was made navigable following pressure from local farmers and land owners.[9]

The Grovers

The early history of Gamnel Wharf is a mystery. It was probably John Grover who saw a business opportunity on the bank of the Wendover Arm, where an old water mill had been dismantled by the Canal Company. The vacant site comprised a triangular piece of land, which provided a good site on which to erect a windmill and build an adjacent wharf at which to send and receive consignments of grain and other commodities.

The date when the windmill was erected is unknown, but Andrew Bryant's map of Tring in 1822 shows a windmill at Gamnel Wharf, while *Pigot's Directory* for 1823 lists the brothers William and James Grover as milling at Gamnel. The earliest actual record of the wharf and premises is in 1829, when they were held by William Grover, while James Grover held the windmill and a house on the same site, at a rateable value of £13.5s.0d.

At some time after 1829, the partnership between the Grover brothers ceased. Why is not known, but, following John Grover's death in 1820, it is known that a dispute - perhaps of a prolonged nature - arose between his sons concerning the terms of his will. In her history of Aldbury, Jean Davis refers to a vestry dispute of 1828, and states that . . . .

---

[9] The abandoned section of the Wendover Arm west of Tring is presently being restored by the Wendover Arm Trust.

"The fact was that, at some time before he died in 1820, John Grover had given up his baker's shop in Aldbury and moved to Tring Wharf. Having acquired some land in North Field, he proceeded to build a house there adjacent to the road, which he left to his son James with the crop and implements and household goods. According to John Clement, watchmaker and Baptist preacher of Tring, James's brother William disputed the will, which finally went to arbitration. James is reported to have said that he was wronged of 'hundreds of pounds'."

For whatever reason, James set out to build and work at nearby Goldfield mill (*Chapter 9*), probably in competition with his brother. The 1839 edition of *Pigot's Directory* lists him at Goldfield windmill, while Gamnel Wharf was run by William Grover & Son in partnership. Moving on to 1841, the Census records William Grover, then aged 60, at Gamnel with his son, Thomas, and the Hilllsdons, father and son, who were later to set up business as millwrights in Chapel Street, Tring (*Chapter 5*). All four are described as millers.

The next public reference to the Grover family appears in January 1843, when a brief notice in the *London Gazette* announced the dissolution of the partnership between William Grover and Son, wharfingers, of Tring Wharf and Paddington; no reason is given, but the inherited rumour is that William Grover became insolvent, which might explain why, in the following month, he disposed of the business to his sons-in-law. The following notice appeared in the *Bucks Advertiser*:

"William Grover, in the town of Tring in the County of Hertfordshire, having on the 28th day of January last disposed of the business of wharfinger, coal and coke merchant and mealman, and dealer in hay, straw, ashes, and other things, lately carried on by him in partnership with Thomas Grover, at Tring Wharf, and at Paddington in the County of Middlesex, under the firm of 'WILLIAM GROVER & SON' to his sons-in-law, William Mead and Richard Bailey.

Messrs. Mead and Bailey beg to announce that they will continue to carry on the same business, upon the said premises, in partnership under the name of 'MEAD & BAILEY'. All debts due to and owing from the said William Grover, will be received and paid by Mead & Bailey."

It is interesting that in both announcements the Grovers describe themselves, not as millers, but as 'wharfingers', which suggests that their principal business activities were the shipment of produce by canal and the resale of imported bulk commodities, such as coal and coke. In an age before the development of road transport and with the nearest railway[10] goods yard some two miles from Tring town centre, the Wendover Arm was not only an important source of water for the Grand Junction Canal, but of commercial importance to the town and surrounding area. Indeed, it is known that the Arm was used not only to convey grain to the windmill at Gamnel, but to that at Wendover (*Chapter 11*) as well, which was also located strategically close to a canal wharf.

---

[10] The London & Birmingham Railway reached Tring in 1838.

After 1843, the Grovers disappear from the story of Gamnel Wharf, while Mead and Bailey continued to offer a diverse range of services, advertising themselves as millers, coal merchants, wharfingers and water carriers; and a few years later, the partners added to their interests by dealing in horse manure, which they shipped out of London. It is likely that Bailey managed the wharf at this time, for in the 1851 Census he describes himself as "Miller and Wharfinger", while Mead appears as "Farmer and Miller" (the Mead family continue to farm in the area).

The Massey family

At this time the workforce numbered around 30 men and the Census returns list all the families living near to each other in the immediate vicinity of the mill. In those days William Mead lived on site, in a handsome house next to the yard, but only owned half the area taken up by the mill of today. But it is open to question whether this was a close-knit and caring community, for a contemporary account relating to one of the mill's employees rather belies this view.

William Massey, who worked as a labourer at the mill, lived with his family on the wharf where he rented a hovel from the miller for a shilling a week. In David Shaw's biography of Gerald Massey,[11] William's eldest son, he writes:

"For this money they [the Massey family] *were given a damp flint stone hut with a roof so low that it was*

---

[11] *Gerald Massey: Chartist, Poet, Radical and Freethinker*, by David Shaw, published 2009 by lulu.com.

impossible for an average adult to stand upright. Having paid the rent, nine shillings remained from William's weekly wage to provide a minimum subsistence."

Gerald Massey was to become a Chartist agitator, later acquiring renown in literary circles as a poet and author. Some years after William's death, Gerald Massey had this to say about his late father's employment at Gamnel Wharf . . . .

"I know a poor old man who, for 40 years, worked for one firm and its three generations of proprietors. He began at a wage of 16s. per week, and worked his way, as he grew older and older, and many necessaries of life grew dearer and dearer, down to six shillings a week, and still he kept working, and would not give up. At six shillings a week he broke a limb, and left work at last, being pensioned off by the firm with a four-penny piece! I know whereof I speak, for that man was my father."

Gamnel tower mill

Regardless of whether the Meads did treat their employees in such a Dickensian manner, their business prospered. It centred on the windmill, which old photographs show to be a brick-built 6-storey tower mill with four double-shuttered patent sails, a fantail, with a gallery on the second floor. The cap was in the 'Kentish style', with an extension at the rear to support the fantail and its stage. It was considered to be a relatively large mill with power sufficient to drive at least three pairs of millstones. While no record exists of the mill's machinery, it was probably comparable to that in the tower mill at nearby

Quainton (*Chapter 13*), which dates from 1832 and, judging by photographs of Gamnel Mill, is of similar external size and appearance.

Thomas Bailey, miller's apprentice

The partnership between Mead & Bailey ended in 1856 on the death of the latter and for the next 88 years the family name of Mead becomes inextricably linked to milling and to other business activities at Gamnel Wharf.

In the year following Richard Bailey's death, his widow, Sarah, bound their son, Thomas, in apprenticeship for five years as miller to Edward Mead. A Tring solicitor drew up the Indenture on 15th April 1857 in wording typical of the time . . . .

> ". . . . the said apprentice his Master shall faithfully serve, his secrets keep, his lawful commands everywhere gladly do . . . . he shall not waste the goods of his Master, nor lend them unlawfully to any. He shall not commit fornication nor contract matrimony within the said term; shall not play Cards or Dice Tables or any other unlawful games; . . . . he shall not haunt Taverns or Playhouses nor absent himself from his Master's service day or night unlawfully . . . ."

How a normal red-blooded young man coped with five years of such conditions is hard to imagine today. Thomas Bailey's mother also had to agree to wash and mend her son's clothes and to supply any medicines that he might require. Although weighted greatly in favour of the master, terms on the

Indenture were not wholly one-sided, as for his part the master agreed to . . . .

> " . . . . *Useth by the best means that he can to teach and instruct, or cause to be taught; finding unto the apprentice sufficient Meat, Drink, Lodging and all other necessaries during the said term* . . . . "

Figure 8.2 Gamnel Wharf Flour Mills, from the yard.

The first use of steam

By the early 1860s the demand for flour was sufficiently high to require a steam engine to be installed to supplement wind power and 19-year old Samuel Bull is recorded in the 1861 Census working at the mill as an 'engine stoker'. Nothing is known about the steam engine, but it is possible that the same practice was followed as that thought to have been adopted at Quainton mill. Here, a small steam engine was installed on the meal floor, its steam being piped from an external boiler house, and the engine coupled to the windmill's spur wheel (and hence millstones, etc) via an iron shaft and cog. This type of arrangement is shown in *plate 21* (although here, nothing is known of the position of the steam engine at Goldfield mill).

Figure 8.3 Gamnel Wharf Mills; an old postcard.

By this time the business at Gamnel Wharf was run by William Mead's third son, Edward, who also rented the windmill at Wendover (*Chapter 11*). Edward Mead had become a busy man, having acquired commercial interests at Bury mill (Watford), Hunton Bridge and Chelsea, where he is believed to have installed the UK's first roller mill.

Figure 8.4 Gamnel Wharf windmill about to be demolished in 1911 - note the hawser attached to the windshaft trailing off to the right of the picture.

Bushell's Boatyard

From about 1850, local man John Bushell was employed by the Meads to build and repair the fleet of barges that brought grain to the mill, mainly from London's docks, returning with cargoes of flour and other commodities. At that time canal boats were often built in small boatyards run by a few men and this applied to the boatyard at Gamnel Wharf, where the craftsmen worked in the open air, even in the most extreme weather.

In 1875, modernisation at the mill resulted in John Bushell's son Joseph taking over the boatyard and developing it into a separate business, while continuing to meet the Meads' requirements for building and maintaining their canal craft.

Modernisation

The Meads' milling business continued to expand. A particular milestone was reached in 1875, when Thomas Mead took the bold step of erecting an imposing brick-built grain mill adjacent to the windmill, its 5-storey height allowing sufficient headroom for a large beam engine of sufficient capacity to drive five pairs of millstones.

The installation of this new machinery did not go without incident, as a local newspaper reports . . . .

*"**Accident** - There was a shifting of the old boiler out of the old engine house at Mr Thomas Mead's flour mill into the new one on Tuesday; and in order to do this, the boiler had to be raised four feet. A small space had been*

left at the end for the jack, and the block underneath slipped when the boiler was raised about two feet, and caused the boiler to run ahead, striking against Lot Denchfield, fracturing his right thigh and left fore arm. Denchfield was at once taken to the County Infirmary at Aylesbury."

Figure 8.5 The remains of Gamnel Wharf windmill.

As the Victorian age progressed, advances in technology swept away old systems. In 1894 a further step was taken when Thomas Mead installed the recently-developed roller system (*Chapter 3, Appendix*), for a time running it in conjunction with the windmill. Then in 1905, the old Bolton & Watt-type beam engine was replaced by a Woodhouse & Mitchell tandem compound condensing engine, rated at 120 hp, which drove the mill until it converted to electric power in 1946.

All across the country, the early 20th century saw the rapid demise of windmills. After some ninety years of faithful service, on 4th May 1911 the tower mill at Gamnel Wharf was demolished. A local newspaper gave the following account . . . .

> *"**Removal of a Landmark** - On May 4th a familiar landmark was demolished. For many years the old windmill where Mr Mead and his ancestors have long carried on their business, has stood at Gamnel. The leisurely business methods of bygone days have had to give place to more up-to-date arrangements and so the ground on which the old mill stood was wanted for an extension of the steam-powered mills. Under the personal direction of Mr W N Mead the structure was first undermined, wooden struts taking the place of the brickwork and when it was ready a steel cable and winch hauled it over."*

As the years passed, other changes came to Mead's flour mill. In 1916, horse transport was supplemented with a Foden steam lorry, this being added to in 1918 by a Napier lorry, the body of which - and of all further lorries up to WWII - was constructed by Bushells. The coal business, which advertisements suggest had been important since the earliest days of Gamnel Wharf, ceased at the outbreak of World War II. Much imported wheat was now used; this was shipped by barge from Brentford to Bulbourne near Tring, where it was transferred to a horse-drawn barge to lighten the load for its passage up the narrow

Wendover Arm. Barge traffic continued on the Arm until about 1946, when it was replaced by road haulage.

The closure of Bushell's boatyard

Joseph Bushell's two sons, Joseph junior and Charles, had taken over the boatyard in 1912, renaming the business Bushell Brothers. But as canal traffic and the market for new barges and repairs declined, more varied work had to be sought.

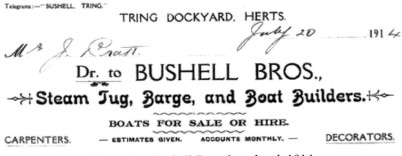

Figure 8.6 Bushell Bros. letterhead, 1914.

Besides their work on narrowboats, the firm is known to have built and repaired pleasure boats, maintenance flats, wide boats, tugs and even a fire float, while their letterhead advertised boats for hire, carpentry and decorating services. One surviving photograph also shows that coal was sold at the boatyard.

Shortly before its closure in 1952, Bushells were constructing and painting coachwork for commercial vehicles. But in local minds the boatyard will always be remembered for its fine narrowboats, a few of which have been preserved by enthusiasts interested in the history of the Grand Union Canal.

Figure 8.7 Bushell Brothers Boat Yard - a wooden canal boat is under construction.

Heygates Flour Mill

Thomas Mead's son, William, died in April, 1941. There being no sons to take over the business, it passed into the control of his executors and trustees. The Mead name finally disappeared from the Gamnel scene in 1944, when the business was taken over by Heygates of Bugbrooke Mills, Northampton, who for some time had been assisting with the running of Gamnel.

Following the end of WWII, the mill's storage silos and warehouses were enlarged and, with the removal of the old south boundary wall (latterly part of the carpenter's shop) to create space for expansion, the last tangible memory of Gamnel

Wharf windmill disappeared.

Today, flour milling continues at Gamnel Wharf but in a manner greatly transformed from its wind and steam milling days. The mechanical shafts, cogs, belts and sets of grindstones have long been replaced by banks of cabinets that house sophisticated filters and grinding rollers serviced by a network of pneumatic feeder pipes. The finished product is no longer

Figure 8.8 William Mead judging wheat.

packed in the two-and-a-half hundredweight (280 lbs.) sacks that carters like William Massey had to deliver into baker's lofts, sometimes carrying each sack up slippery external wooden steps or ladders. Today, Gamnel's modern automated packing plant fills 32 kilos (70 lbs.) sacks, which are then neatly palleted, swathed in polythene sheet, and loaded onto lorries by forklift truck. Some flour also leaves the mill in bulk transporters.

As in the days of the windmill, only two men are needed to operate the plant. But whereas in former times the two millers could process half a ton of grain per hour, today's electrically-driven equipment operating under computer control, can mill

12 tons per hour; or put another way, 100,000 tons of wheat is milled in a year resulting in 76,000 tons of flour, the bulk of the waste going into animal feed. The mill employs a workforce of 80, and 16 trucks deliver its products to outlets throughout the south of England.

Figure 8.9 A Sentinel steam lorry, complete with solid tyres and acetylene lamps, but lacking an offside door - and no need for a heater.

Chapter 9

GOLDFIELD MILL (TRING)

Figure 9.1 Postcard showing Goldfield mill. Note the patent sail shutters.

The name 'Goldfield'

Local folklore assumes that the windmill acquired its name from the surrounding fields of yellow buttercups, which in Victorian times stretched from Western Road to Icknield Way. However, the area where the mill was built is shown on old maps by its medieval field name of *Goole Field*, which over the years may have become corrupted to *Goldfield*. The mill stood, and continues to stand, at the top of a steep and narrow lane that crossed the Icknield Way and then led down to the long-forgotten hamlet of Miswell. This lane became known as

Windmill Lane; later, after the road was widened and surfaced, it became Miswell Lane.

Figure 9.2 Tring c.1834, showing the windmill symbol at the junction of Icknield Way and Miswell Lane (below *Miswell*).

The Grover family

The first miller was James Grover, a member of a family of wharfingers and millers who worked the windmill at Gamnel Wharf (*Chapter 8*) beside the Wendover Arm of the Grand Junction Canal. At some time c.1830 - exactly when is unknown - James left Gamnel Wharf to live at and work the new windmill that he, presumably, had erected at Goldfield.

Goldfield mill (*plate 19*) is a medium-sized tower mill of four storeys, built of red brick. Old photographs show that it was fitted with four double-shuttered patent sails, a fantail and a cap of rounded pepper-pot shape surmounted with a ball finial. No information survives about the mill's machinery, but some remnants remain in place: the great spur wheel (wood on an iron centre) and an auxiliary shaft (iron - *plate 21* - possibly a drive shaft from the steam engine) make attractive features over what is now a first floor sitting room, while some of the iron aligning wheels remain in the cap (the rollers are obscured from view). The complex around the mill includes two cottages c.1789 and a large granary barn put up *c.*1840. Although the elevated site must have been chosen with care, the wind currents never proved entirely satisfactory for driving the mill, being unreliable during the summer months.

The 1841 Census lists those at the mill as James Grover (then a widower of 50) and his two sons, Jabez and William, two daughters and William Cartwright, a carter. There was possibly another helper, Osborn Hooker (believed to be *Rooker*), a journeyman miller who lodged at a beer house at Frogmore End. Charles Grover - described as a 'journeyman miller' - and his family occupied a separate dwelling, but they do not appear in later Census records.

The windmill probably did the job for which it was designed without incident, thereby supporting the miller and his dependants, for nothing is known of it during the first 20 years of its life. However, in later years there are occasional reports of the mill and its millers and of the declining prosperity that typified windmill operations increasingly during the second half of the 19th century.

Goldfield Mills Tring

Photo C. A. Howlett

Figure 9.3 Goldfield mill - viewed from the end of the present Fantail Lane. The field in the foreground is now covered with houses.

In 1862 James Grover died and the partnership between father and sons was dissolved, Jabez and William parting company, with William remaining as miller. The reason for this parting - which long persisted in local folklore - was that the brothers quarrelled violently, which led to William murdering Jabez with a coal shovel; thereafter his ghost was said to haunt the staircase of the Mill House. But although William might well have crowned Jabez with a shovel, there are no reports of this allegedly grisly event in newspapers of the time and it is likely that Jabez died peacefully in his bed, for the grave of a Jabez Grover, dated 1889, can be seen in New Mill Chapel burial ground.

In 1869, a local news report tells of William Grover entering into dispute with the authorities in Tring over the non-payment of rates. He was duly summoned to appear before the magistrates at Berkhamsted Petty Sessions, where he claimed that he had settled a rate demand for £1.2s.6d. on his land, but was later charged unjustly again for the mill unjustly. His case was not viewed sympathetically by the bench, for he was assessed for a further £3 with - to rub salt in the wound - £1.5s.6d. costs.

The Liddington family

About this time William took as his assistant a nephew, 16-year old Thomas Liddington, who by the mid-1870s had moved his family into Mill House and had also acquired sufficient experience to be classed as a 'master miller'. Thomas worked the mill assisted by Henry Liddington and Harry Robinson, who lived next door. By then milling was not Thomas's sole business activity; dealing in corn and retailing flour and other foodstuffs had also become important.

In 1876 the mill was put up for sale by auction, being described in the particulars as a complex covering a three-acre site . . . .

"Messrs. Woodman & Son have been favoured with instructions to sell by auction, at the Rose & Crown Hotel, Tring, on Friday November 3rd, 1876 , IN ONE LOT:

The valuable freehold estate comprising a well-built substantial WINDMILL, fitted with three pairs of stones in good working order; neat brick and slated eight-roomed RESIDENCE with extensive GARDEN, CORN

WAREHOUSE, CARPENTER'S SHOP, STABLE, PIGGERIES, foreman's COTTAGE, small enclosed FARM YARD, GRANARY, DRYING KILN, BLACKSMITH'S SHOP, CHAISE HOUSE, a neat ORCHARD planted with choice fruit trees, and a valuable piece of BUILDING LAND, the whole occupying an area of about three acres, tithe free and land-tax redeemed . . . . "

Although not recorded, it appears that Thomas Liddington bought the property. In retrospect, this proved to be a poor investment, for by then milling was becoming a more highly mechanised trade and as the years passed Goldfield windmill could not compete favourably in the flour trade with Thomas Mead's increasingly modern steam mill at Gamnel Wharf. In 1888 Thomas Liddington was forced to file for bankruptcy, the application being heard in Aylesbury County Court where it was recorded that his liabilities amounted to £1,176.3s.3d. with a deficiency of £269.11s.7d. Described as a miller and farmer, Thomas claimed that the causes of his failure were a decline in trade, bad debts and other losses incurred due to his horse and cattle dying. But this was not the only disaster to befall the Liddington family, for Henry's dealings with customers were not always scrupulously honest (*see Liddington in Chapter 4*).

James Wright, the last miller

Who held the mill during the next few years is unknown, but after 1888 it was worked by White & Putnam, a partnership that operated several local mills. At some stage - the records of exactly when are conflicting - James Wright, the miller at

Hastoe steam mill, about a mile and a half from Tring, took over at Goldfield. He is shown as being miller at both sites until about 1902 by which time he had moved to Goldfield.

Being familiar with steam milling it was natural that James should use auxiliary power at Goldfield and a 6 hp steam engine was duly installed to work a pair of grinding stones, the windmill driving an oat crusher to provide animal feed when the wind was favourable. James Wright's son, Herbert, born in the Mill House in 1897, is quoted as saying . . . .

> ". . . . when I was ten years of age I was strong enough to stoke the engine boiler and maintain the water pressure as well as help the miller dress the stones when they had to be sharpened."

Herbert Wright goes on relate that during his father's tenure at Goldfield, the mill was owned by Thomas Butcher & Son, bankers, of Tring High Street. How Butcher's Bank[12] came to own the mill is unknown, but it seems possible that they acquired it following Thomas Liddington's bankruptcy, perhaps as a foreclosure on an outstanding mortgage.

The two systems of wind and steam power ran in tandem until around 1903 when the sails of the windmill were removed. Even so, it could be that the milling business was

---

[12] The head office of Butcher's Bank was situated in Tring High Street, in the building now occupied by NatWest Bank. First created by Thomas Butcher in 1836 as an adjunct to his seed and corn business in the town, the bank continued trading until c.1900, when it was taken over by its London agent. Following other acquisitions and mergers, Butcher's Bank eventually became part of NatWest Bank.

still not yielding sufficient profit, for two years later the
Bucks Advertiser reported that over an acre of grazing land
at Goldfield had been sold for the sum of £9.2s.6d.

The viability of the mill at this time appears to have depended
largely upon a contact with the Rothschild Tring Park estate for
crushing oats as for animal feed on its many farms. The
contract ending in 1908, James left Goldfield to take over the
tenancy of Brook End water and steam mill situated some three
miles away on the border of Ivinghoe and Pitstone, taking its
water supply from the Whistle Brook. He is recorded here in
1911 as 'miller, baker and confectioner'.[13]

The windmill abandoned

Goldfield mill was then put up for auction by William Brown
& Co., *The Bucks Herald* reporting that . . . .

> *"Considerable interest was manifested in Tring and the
> surrounding district regarding the sale of Goldfield
> Windmill, one of the most well known landmarks in the
> neighbourhood. The property comprised the windmill;
> two dwelling houses; numerous outbuildings; and a
> valuable meadow of about two acres, with a long
> frontage to Miswell Lane. The property stands at a high
> and healthy elevation and commands most perfect
> scenery of the Vale of Aylesbury and the Chiltern Hills,
> and the downs and woodlands of the Ashridge estate.
> Messrs. W. Brown & Co. submitted the whole property*

---

[13] The nearby Ford End watermill - also on the Whistle Brook - remains in
working order and is opened to the public.

by auction on October 30th but the bidding did not reach the reserve figure and is now to be dealt with privately."

In 1911 Brown & Co. again advertised the complex, but the outcome is unknown. It is likely that milling had ceased following James Wright's departure, for by this time small milling concerns saw their business dwindling in the face of competition from much larger and more efficient roller mills. (Herbert Wright records that after his father took over Brook End watermill, *"he was forced to give up"* in 1913, being unable to compete with the large milling firms.) However, the living accommodation at Goldfield continued to be used and Miriam Wright, who in the period 1916-21 lived with her parents in one of the cottages, remembered that during WW I soldiers used the top windows of the mill for signal practice.

Restoration of the granary and cottage

In 1919, the entire complex was eventually sold - it is believed for £1,000 - to a Mrs Cunningham from Rhodesia. This lady then constructed a dwelling for herself and her family from the granary and attached cottage, later turning the barn into a bungalow for her daughter. When Mrs Cunningham died in 1955, the house passed to Peter Bell, a journalist for the *British Farmer and Stockbreeder* magazine, but the windmill continued in its state of dereliction.

In 1946 the tenancy of the adjacent Mill House cottage was acquired by a well-known local lady, Phyllis Thomas, librarian at the Akeman Street Zoological Museum, who lived there for many years until forced to leave by her increasing frailty (she

Figure 9.4 *c.*1966, Phyllis Thomas (left) seated on an old millstone outside the front door of Goldfield Mill House cottage.

died in 1990 aged 102). In 1973 she wrote a letter to *Hertfordshire Countryside* magazine in which she said . . . .

". . . . I remember Herbert Wright as a small boy helping his father . . . . My sisters and I would frequently walk up Miswell Lane (in very truth a country lane in those days where one could gather primroses and blue and white violets) to purchase eggs and other farm produce from Mrs Wright. It was a great treat to be allowed to climb the ladder-staircase of the mill, all white with flour dust, and gaze through one of the little windows, at the lovely, unspoilt Chiltern countryside . . . .[14] *All around were*

---

[14] The mill's cap is now a sitting room with a good view towards Mentmore.

meadows and farm land and, directly in front, the famous 'goldfields', a sheet of yellow buttercups."

The Mill House and its adjoining granary now form a single dwelling, one that has been sympathetically restored and modernised by its present owners. Some of the original fittings have been incorporated, including internal doors (complete with their latches), cupboard doors, wooden beams, iron brackets and a brick-lined cellar. The cast iron pump from the granary remains, while the old well it tapped into is hidden beneath the kitchen floor. Outside, old bricks have been re-used in some of the paved areas and two of the windmill's grinding stones now make attractive garden features.

Figure 9.5 Goldfield Mill House and cottage, drawn by
Peter Bell in 1964.

During the 1960s, when new housing was being built in the Icknield Way area, Tring Council ensured that the sad-looking old windmill would not be forgotten entirely by naming three new roads *Windmill Way, Mill View Road, and Fantail Lane.*

Restoration of the windmill

The windmill's fortunes improved some years later when an American artist applied for permission to convert both the windmill and adjacent barn to a dwelling and to add an extension to form guest accommodation. But conversion of an old building is not a simple matter and this was explained in one of a series of articles featuring unusual homes, which appeared in the *Post Echo* of September 1979 . . . .

". . . . the previous owner gathered in the barns and milking sheds which huddle around the old mill and made the whole thing into a place of rambling spaciousness. There's a good reason for this. A windmill may be very stout - walls start at two and a half feet thick at the bottom and taper to one and one and a half at the top - and snug, but it's a problem to put water pipes in. On outside walls they disfigure the place: same goes for the inside walls.

So the builder left them out, which ruled out a kitchen and bathroom in the tower . . . . The original lead cap is now an ornament in the back garden. The man who converted the mill was so concerned with retaining the original effect, and so unconcerned with the expense, that he put in a glass fibre replacement, impregnated with copper crystals. . . ."

Figure 9.6 Goldfield windmill prior to its conversion to a dwelling.

When the windmill was again offered for sale in 2004, the sales particulars described five circular rooms, some with the old beams and timber cog wheels, and a tower room with spectacular views. Goldfield windmill now claims the distinction of Grade II listing, as well as being the only remaining tower mill in Dacorum.

Chapter 10

HAWRIDGE MILL

Figure 10.1 Hawridge windmill in retirement.

The smock mill replaced

Hawridge tower mill (*plate 15*) sits at the crest of Ray's Hill behind the ancient Full Moon public house. When viewed from Cholesbury and Hawridge commons, the mill's graceful outline considerably enhances the pleasing scene, although the field to the rear gives the most complete view of the mill.

Dating from 1883, the new tower mill - which replaced the earlier smock mill (*Chapter 6*) - must have been among the last of its kind to be erected in Britain. Built at a time when traditional wind-driven milling was giving way to more modern methods, the mill was to have a short working life. Indeed, one cannot help but wonder about the business case for a new windmill at this date, for a steam-driven mill already existed on the site; perhaps the cost of hauling coal up to the isolated common had something to do with it.

As events turned out, the most interesting aspects of Hawridge windmill's history date from the period following its retirement, when, having been converted into a private dwelling, it was from time to time peopled by some well-known literary and artistic personalities.

The tower mill's early life

Hawridge mill was built by Hillsdons, a family firm of millwrights from Tring (*Chapter 5*) at a cost of £300, a price that was probably very reasonable due to its machinery, one pair of sweeps and its curb being inherited from the earlier smock mill. The new mill was ten feet taller overall than its predecessor, which with its narrow curb accounts for an

Figure 10.2 Hawridge tower mill in its heyday.

elegantly slender profile. Nearby stood the existing steam-powered mill, which an early photograph shows housed in a separate building, its boiler being serviced by an imposingly-large brick chimney. At some stage in the windmill's life a grain store was added to the base of the tower, later to be converted into a dwelling.[15]

---

[15] For technical details of the mill, see the Appendix to this chapter.

The records are unclear as to the mill's early ownership. It is believed to have been built for Daniel Dwight, a local farmer, and that while awaiting its first tenant it was driven by the millwrights. However, the new mill soon changed hands; in January 1885, the following advertisement appeared in both *The Miller* magazine and the *Bucks Advertiser* . . . .

Figure 10.3 Tom Robinson, the last miller

"To be let or sold, with immediate possession, the freehold newly-erected wind and steam flour mill, with residence, stabling, and garden, situate at Hawridge."

It appears that the mill did not sell outright, for Daniel Dwight is still recorded as owner in a trade directory of 1891. He then leased the premises to Daniel Wright, who in the following year engaged an experienced miller, Thomas Robinson. Robinson, a Northamptonshire man, was well used to steam power having previously been miller at Brook End water and steam mill, Pitstone, a mill that drove four pairs of stones. He moved into the premises with his wife and nine children, later becoming tenant and working the mill until its closure in 1912. Thomas Robinson died in 1941 and is buried in the graveyard of Cholesbury church.

Gilbert Cannan and friends

Life in a windmill appears to hold special appeal to people of artistic temperament; Goldfield, Wendover and Hawridge windmills were all once occupied by those involved in the world of the Arts. Thus it was that in 1913 an aspiring young author, poet, and playwright and his wife fell in love with Hawridge mill, having spent some months in a rented cottage at Bellingdon a mile or so down the road from Cholesbury Common.

Gilbert Cannan (1884-1955) and Mary Barrie (ex-wife of writer J M Barrie) were seeking the solitude of the countryside, which Gilbert thought would have a beneficial effect on his work. In the early summer of 1913 the Cannans, together with their two enormous dogs, took up residence in the tile-hung Mill House that stands to the right of the entrance drive to the mill. But more important to Gilbert was the windmill, which he intended to turn into his own private haven and place of work. He wrote to a friend *"We've taken a windmill to clear out to in the Chilterns, and I'm to have a study looking towards the four corners of the Heavens and the earth" (Chapter 12)*. Gilbert obviously drew his desired inspiration from the panoramic views of the surrounding countryside, for during this period novels, plays, poetry and translations poured from his pen and he succeeded in achieving a modest literary reputation.

Inside the windmill, the local carpenter was engaged to fit shelves in the study for the Cannans' huge collection of books; a tall desk was installed where Gilbert worked - either standing or sitting on a high stool - and a Russian artist friend painted a

Figure 10.4 Mary Barrie and Gilbert Cannan.

frieze around the walls. Other aspects of interior design were suggested and carried out by Mary. She decorated the walls of the circular living room with great flower patterns, cutting out and pasting up each flower, fern and leaf herself; although not to everyone's taste, all their guests admired her originality. A spiral staircase was fitted and a dado of brightly-coloured frescos adorned the dining room.[16]

At first, the couple enjoyed their rustic life. The garden of the Mill House was already planted out and Mary acquired part of a paddock adjoining the mill to enlarge the grounds. A courtyard was laid and tubs planted with shrubs and flowers. Gilbert joined the local cricket club and occasionally played bowls in the adjacent public house, *The Full Moon*, including in the party any of the Cannans' frequent weekend visitors.

---

[16] Alas, nothing now remains of the frieze, frescos or spiral staircase.

Cholesbury has probably never seen such a lively time as the period of Gilbert Cannan's occupancy of the windmill. Weekend evenings saw pastimes, such as poetry readings, playing the pianola, philosophical talk and performances by the guests of plays written by Gilbert. The artistic luminaries of the day who stayed there, or in the village, included writers D H Lawrence, Katherine Mansfield and Compton Mackenzie; and the painters Vladimir Polunin and Mark Gertler. In Gertler's colourful *Gilbert Cannan at his windmill* (*plate 18*), the tapering windmill flanked by trees provides the background to the main subject who is depicted standing between his two dogs, one of which, *Porthos*, was used as the model for *Nana* in J M Barrie's *Peter Pan*. Reputed to have taken two years to complete, the painting is now on display in the Ashmolean Museum, Oxford.

But the idyll was not to last. The Great War broke out; Gilbert's fragile mental health began to show the first signs of collapse; his marriage was failing, eventually ending in 1918 following an affair with their maid, who became pregnant.

Following WWI, Gilbert wrote and translated a great deal. He also travelled and during an absence in America his mistress, Gwen Wilson, a radiantly beautiful art student, married the third member of what had become a *ménage à trios*, the industrialist and financier Henry Mond. The result was that Cannan suffered an irreversible mental breakdown and spent his remaining years confined to a private psychiatric hospital where he died in 1955.

The mill's later life

Shortly after the Cannans left the mill in 1916, the tenancy was taken by one of their friends, the American actress Doris Keane (1881-1945), who used the windmill as her country retreat. The artistic connection continued until the 1930s when a Chelsea portrait and landscape artist, Bernard Adams (1888-1965), conducted an art school in the mill.

A description of the mill at this time appears in *English Windmills* (Vol. 2), although this was concerned with its structural condition rather than its colourful tenants. . . .

> *"This is a circular brick mill standing in private grounds behind the old converted mill house . . . It last worked sixteen years ago, when it was grinding standard flour. Since it ceased working a cottage has been built against the mill, apparently incorporating part of its lower floor. One of the sails was shortened at that time as its length interfered with the work on the roof."*

In 1937, the Windmill Section of the Society for the Protection of Ancient Buildings stepped in to carry out necessary repairs. One account states that the windmill was transferred to Cholesbury Parish shortly before the outbreak of WWII., but this seems unlikely.

Hawridge windmill experienced another change in its fortunes during WWII., when it was used as a look-out post (it is nice to imagine its being inhabited by a platoon of Home Guard similar to Captain Mainwaring's); local folklore is that its sails

Figure 10.5 Hawridge windmill c.1932.

were used as semaphore signals - amusing but unlikely. What is certain is that it afterwards fell into disrepair and dereliction. One sail blew off during a gale in the early 1950s and another collapsed.

The mill had to wait until 1968 to be completely restored by its then owner, Don Saunders, an engineer at British Aerospace. He designed and built new hollow steel spars, painted red and white, which were winched into position to replace the mill's original sails.

Hawridge mill has had several owners since its post-war restoration, with the artistic connection continuing with Mrs Saunders, a former Tiller Girl, and Sir David Hatch, a comedian and later Managing Director of BBC Radio.

The mill is now tastefully furnished as a private home with a spacious kitchen installed in what was once the meal floor. Some of the mill's equipment survives in the cap, where the supporting rollers, rack and alignment wheels can be seen together with a substantial iron windshaft held firmly in place at its tail end by a roller bearing. The winding gear, once driven by the fantail (that fitted today is for purely for show), also remains in place together with its spindle, rack and pinion (similar to the gear shown in *plates 24, 27* and *28*).

Downstairs in the sitting room appears a large cast iron wheel, some eight feet in diameter, propped up against one of the walls. What it *was* is something of a mystery. The fine machining suggests a degree of precision unlike windmill equipment, while there is no obvious sign of wooden teeth having been attached. Furthermore, the aperture for the spindle appears too small to accommodate an upright shaft. What it might have been - if indeed it came from the mill - was the steam engine's flywheel (the 12 hp steam engine at Wendover mill is recorded as having driven an 11ft diameter flywheel!)

APPENDIX: technical details of Hawridge mill

English Windmills (Vol.2), provides the following brief description of Hawridge windmill in 1932 . . . .

> *"The four sails are complete, but the shutters have been removed. The vanes of the fantail are missing, but the staging remains. The gallery is complete. The cap is of the ogee shape and is apparently covered with zinc sheeting. The whole of the tower is tarred."*

The ever-helpful writer on windmills, Stanley Freese, recorded the following technical description (c.1939):

> *"The reefing gear was controlled by external chain and weights suspended from a 'Y' wheel on the fan stage; and the fly was of the 8-vaned pattern. From this fantail a wormshaft passed horizontally over the curb to drive a vertical countershaft, at the foot of which a pinion engaged with the iron cog-ring upon the inner face of the curb, as at Wendover and Quainton. In common with the latter mills, Hawridge is provided with a 'shot' curb, that is to say a floating chain of bearing rollers free of both the curb and cap; but in the present instance the rollers are shorter and more sharply tapered than at Wendover. They are hollow, with two slots at the end for positioning the inner casting cone. Two check wheels are suspended by iron arms to run against the curb beneath the cog-ring; one at the tail, and one on the right-hand side, to correspond with the luffing gear on the left-hand. The tail bearing of the iron windshaft is situated in the tail of the small cap, so that the shaft actually extends*

back over the curb of the mill; and upon the shaft is a two-piece eight-armed iron brake wheel measuring only 7 or 8 ft. in diameter, its wooden cogs engaging with an iron wallower upon an iron upright shaft, but all the gear below the windshaft was cleared out early in the war [WWI].

"There are believed to have been two pairs of under-driven stones in the mill, driven by a wooden spur; and an additional two pairs in the wooden building of the steam mill."

Figure 10.6 The chimney of the original steam mill being demolished in 1884.

Chapter 11

WENDOVER MILL

A massive mill

What photographs there are of Wendover tower mill (*plate 22*) do little to prepare visitors for the imposing bastion that confronts them when they first turn into the footpath between Aylesbury Road and Dobbins Lane. Although long shorn of its sails and fantail, this tower mill retains sufficient majesty to convey the clear impression that, in its day, it must have been an emperor among windmills. The author Stanley Freese had this to say about it . . . .

Figure 11.1 Wendover mill
sketched by the last miller.

"with its massive walls and broad outline, and its colossal cap - possibly the heaviest in England - Wendover Mill might have been converted from an old fortress or castle keep."

An apt description.

Construction

Wendover mill was built by John Phillips (1776-1843) but it is possible that his father, Zachariah (1745-97), a prominent local landowner, commenced the work. It is not known exactly when the mill was erected for although the date "AD 1796" appears on a stone plaque above the front entrance, milling did not commence until 1804. It is recorded that the initials "J.S. & J.T. 1804" are carved into one of the massive internal beams on the second floor, probably by its millwrights, but these are no longer visible. The mill's situation was possibly chosen for close proximity to the wharf of the recently opened Wendover Arm of the Grand Junction Canal.

The mill is said to have been built from 500 tons of bricks carried down in panniers by donkeys from a kiln in the locality of Cholesbury, possibly along the ancient packway now called Hogtrough Lane (Freese *MSS.*, 1939). The structure, a 5-storey tower mill, is among the largest in Britain. Its octagonal walls - unusual for a tower mill - stand approximately 66ft high, to which the cap adds a further 18ft. At the base they are 26ft in diameter and 3ft thick, the latter dimension being plainly apparent when looking through the lower windows from within the mill. The walls taper to about 2ft in thickness and 20ft in diameter at the top, their corners being nicely chamfered just below the cap to lead up to the curb.[17]

The mill originally had a gallery at second floor level (*fig. 11.2*) but this was removed in 1947 when extensive repairs were made; the present gallery at cap level is a recent addition

---

[17] The iron ring that sits on top of the tower and carries the rotatable cap.

constructed to ease roof maintenance; leakage has been a recurring and expensive problem to deal with. A tall chimney stack was also built onto the south side of the mill at some time after windmilling ceased, for it would otherwise have impeded the fanstage as it revolved.

Although the fanstage and fantail are long gone, the worm-gear that the fantail drove remains in place, together with cross-bars that permitted hand-winding, necessary when there was a very sudden change in wind direction. This gearing connects, via a vertical spindle, with an iron rack of some 300 iron teeth, set into a cill that extends around the circumference of the cap (*plate 24*). In operation, the fantail engaged with the rack, via the worm-gear and spindle, to rotate the cap and

Figure 11.2 Wendover mill showing fanstage, gallery and engine house.

wind the sails. The 30 iron rollers upon which the cap revolved also remain in place (some just visible above the rack, *plate 24*).

The cap is of wood and much larger than those at Quainton, Goldfield and Hawridge tower mills. Its base consists of four cross members that are mortised at each end into two massive beams that extend across the mill. Above this, 24 substantial rafters arch upwards to a pinnacle, forming the frame that supports the roof - quite spectacular as one looks up at its apex (*plate 23*). The roof's interior is clad with wooden boarding, its exterior with zinc sheeting.

Notable among the mill's former machinery were its upright shaft - reported to have been a ship's mast - and its 4-ton, 18ft iron windshaft, which remains in place and which the millwright Derek Ogden, who worked on the mill in the 1960s, claimed to be the biggest that he had ever seen (*plate 25*). Also remaining and clearly visible from behind the mill, is the iron centre cross on which the stocks that carried the sails were mounted. Originally, the sails were of the 'simple' variety but these were later replaced; when the mill was sold in 1875, the auctioneer's catalogue described them as being . . . .

> "*of modern construction, with all the latest improvements, two of which are recently new, and the Fan* [fantail] *will be found good and efficient.*"

Although long gone in Freese's time, he describes the sails as having been "*double-shuttered anti-clock patents*", which can be seen at *fig. 11.3*.

Steam milling

At some point in its life wind power was supplemented with a 12 hp steam engine installed in an engine-house built onto the south side of the mill . . .

> "*. . . the former windmill at Wendover was converted to steam power because the building of houses near to it affected the currents of air. The late Mr. F Purssell, the*

miller, said there was great difficulty when the wind shifted suddenly into the opposite quarter, and the sails started to revolve backwards. The sails had to be wound round by hand to bring them into the wind again."

In Buckinghamshire (G.Elland, 1923)

Stanley Freese describes the machinery as . . . .

"an exceptionally fine expansion engine, no doubt the best ever used in a Buckinghamshire windmill . . . . starting from cold at 7.30 a.m., she would soon grind corn with about 40 lbs. of steam, but would not operate the sack hoist until about 11.30 . . . . sometimes the sack hoist was driven all day in order to replenish the exceptionally capacious bins."

Figure 11.3 Wendover mill, showing its double-shuttered patent sails and fantail in place, also the engine chimney.

138

A flue from the engine's boiler passed underground to a tall brick-built chimney in the centre of the mill yard. Although it is not known when the steam engine was installed, it is known that it was by Hillsdons of Tring (*Chapter 5*).

Milling is believed to have continued using both wind and steam, but having been damaged severely by a storm the sails were removed in 1904.

The occupants

Wendover Mill had a number of occupiers up to 1875. Local trade directories list Thomas Horwood and Thomas Andrews as millers in 1842 and 1850 respectively; the 1851 Census lists Charles Burton. In 1861 the diary of Thomas Grace of Tring records that he accompanied his brother-in-law, Edward Mead, to look over the mill and that Edward agreed to pay £100 a year in rent. Mead operated the mill until 1869 when Thomas Edward Biggs took over.

In 1875, due to the expiry of the lease, the mill was offered for sale by auction. The name Zachariah Phillips appears on the auctioneer's ground plan, which suggests that the freehold remained in the possession of the original owners, the Phillips family. The sale was conducted by Reader & Son at the *Bell Hotel*, Aylesbury. Their catalogue describes the property as a . .

"Brick-built, octagon-shaped, roomy
FREEHOLD WINDMILL
of five stories, driving three pairs of stones,
with the whole of the gearing complete
also, attached thereto, a

and boiler, with high Shaft, driving two pairs of Stones . . . . "

In addition to the windmill were granary, store houses, cart sheds, stables, the miller's house, out-houses, yard and garden. The catalogue goes on to describe in detail the mill's structure and equipment (see Appendix).

The mill was bought by William Purssell for £1,000, but others ran it for the names of Francis Beesley (1877) and George Butterfield (1883) appear in the records. On William Purssell's death in 1887, his son Frank took over from Butterfield and continued to operate the mill until his death in 1922.

In his account, Freese suggests that in its early life the windmill was unsuccessful commercially and it was not until Frank Purssell's time that business began to look up . . . .

> ". . . . he took her over from a Mr Butterfield. Steadily the business improved under his management, and he confounded the pessimists by building up a very flourishing and successful trade, which was still very good when he passed away in 1922 . . . . mostly English wheat was ground in the old days, some of it coming by canal to Wendover Wharf, but with the steam engine they latterly ground much Russian barley and American maize, etc. and flour was made until about 1912; generally speaking there was a loss of about 7 lbs. per bushel."

Following Frank's death in 1922 his son Basil carried on, but by then business was beginning to decline, probably due to competition from larger and more efficient roller mills. By

Figure 11.4 Wendover mill soon after conversion to a dwelling.

1925 the mill was only working two days a week due to *"difficulties of the trade"*. In the following year, the General Strike and its coal shortage led to the mill's closure. The machinery was removed in 1929 and the engine house and chimney were demolished two years later.

The windmill in domestic life

By the time of its closure, the mill's floors were in poor structural condition with rot affecting some of the joists, probably due to damp seeping through flaws in the bonding of the brickwork. The mill's cap was also perishing and there was talk of demolishing the top two floors. Happily this drastic action was avoided and in 1931 the mill was converted to a private house. Freese, writing during the 1930s, reports that . . . .

". . . . some big long irons or bolts were inserted by which the weak fourth floor is now practically suspended from the curb of the mill, whilst the fifth floor has two iron girders set into the wall just below, giving support to the rotten ends of the two main joists. New staircases have been installed . . . . and the ground floor has been converted to a cosy living room by Miss Marion Fawcett, the actress and playwright, who is now the tenant, whilst the second floor contains two comfortable bedrooms and a bathroom, the upper floors being vacant ."

Miss Fawcett, who leased the mill for 15s. a week, continued the tenant until 1946 when the mill again fell into disuse. Basil Purssell, writing to the *Bucks Herald* in October 1954, stated that . . . .

"In October 1948, when a gale blew in part of the back cap, Mr Freese was a great help. Together with a London workman, Mr. Carew, who had been working therein that summer, he repaired the roof temporarily for £50 and it was a courageous job. . . . the late Mrs. Frank Purssell planned the preservation of the mill back in 1931, the idea being to convert it into a comfortable home . . . after that considerable sums of money were spent on maintenance both by the owners and the leaseholder, London actress Marion Fawcett."

By 1953 the mill was again in a poor state of repair and at risk of demolition. It was offered for sale and an advertisement in the *New Statesman* caught the eye of Kenneth and Margaret Roberton, who bought the mill and moved in on Coronation Day, 1953. Again, the *Bucks Herald . . . .*

"The new owner, who is the well-known musician Kenneth Roberton, spent a further £600 this summer on renovation."

The domed roof was rebuilt in the mid 1960s making the top two floors habitable and from the 1970s until his death in 2003 Kenneth Roberton used them as the base for his music publishing business, Roberton Publications. His obituary in *The Bucks Herald* stated that he was a tireless campaigner for the town's interests, helped to found the Wendover Society, as well as fighting for the rights of residents and battling against developments that he felt would adversely affect the town.

A further piece of structural work on the cap is recorded in an article on the mill in the *Bucks Advertiser* in June, 1971 . . . .

"in the summer of 1969, the familiar black cap was replaced with a shining white aluminium one . . . ."

. . . . that the present occupier had to replace when the aluminium was discovered to be leaking through its joints. The cap is now clad with zinc sheeting, the fastenings of which are sheltered from the rain by fold-over joints.

Today the windmill, which is Grade II listed, is a very comfortable family home. Its five levels contain five bedrooms, three reception rooms, three bathrooms and a kitchen - but looking back at some of the old repair bills, one cannot help forming the impression that those who would live in an old windmill need a deep pocket!

APPENDIX: auctioneer's particulars (1875)

Engine House

A superior 12-horse-power horizontal Steam Engine (by Hillsdon, Tring), working expansively with 11-inch cylinders, 2ft.4 stroke, large fly wheel (11 feet diameter), steam and exhaust pipes, with governors, pump, &c., bed plate, and brick foundation. An excellent Cornish boiler (only recently put in), 18ft. by 4ft.6, with flue 2ft.3 in diameter, dome, safety valve, pressure gauge, water gauge, and the brick setting thereof. Hand-force pump for feeding boiler.

The Mill

GROUND FLOOR.—Crank shaft from steam engine, 5½-inch diameter, and 14ft. long, driving two pairs of wheat stones on first floor, on cast-iron upright frames, with plummer blocks and brasses, carrying two bevel wheels, driving pinions, on stone spindle, with iron bridge-trees and brass steps, iron rising screws one drum on end of shaft, for driving dressing tackle on 1st Floor two meal bins and shoots, jogging screen for offals, sack jumper, and step ladder.

FIRST FLOOR.—Two pairs of 4ft. wheat stones (driven by steam power), with damsels, wood hoppers and casing, stone spindles, bevel wheels and pinions, iron shaft, driving pulley, cast-iron housings, housings, and wood shoot. One 21-inch lay shaft, 9ft.6 long, with plummer blocks and three pulleys, driving the 3ft.6 dressing machine, with 16-inch cylinder, pulleys, plummer blocks and shaft, complete in deal case flour bin, offal bin.

SECOND FLOOR.—Spur wheel and three stone nuts and spindles, bridge trees, rising screws, and governors, three jogging screens to part the offals, three meal bins, three spouts, apparatus and chain for hoisting by steam power.

THIRD OR STONE FLOOR.—Two pairs of wheat and one pair of barley stones, 4ft. and 4ft. 6 in diameter, with damsels, wood hoppers, and casings, stone spindles, spur wheels and pinions, iron shaft, driving pulley, cast iron housings, and wood shoots one lay shaft, about 10ft. long, with hanger and plummer blocks, bevel pinions for driving smutter, dressing machine, and bolting mill one crown wheel, on wallow shaft and iron pinion one dressing machine, 4ft.6 long, with 16-inch cylinder, and apparatus feed, &c. one horizontal smutting machine, 2ft.2 long, 16 inches diameter, with shaft, pulleys, &c. bolting machine, 6ft. long, with spindle, pulley, plummer blocks, &c.

FOURTH FLOOR. —Hoppers to smut machine two others six large bins.

FIFTH STORY.—Iron wind shaft, with large iron boss and break wheel cast iron wallow wheel, working into break wheel, with oak upright shaft, circular rack, and hand-gear to fan-tail self-acting hoisting tackle, with wood barrel break and lever, and about 84 feet of quarter-inch chain.

YARD.—53 feet of smoke flue, brick smoke shaft, base 6ft. square, height about 55 feet.

146

Chapter 12

WINDMILLS IN LITERATURE

In prose

Could there be a more picturesque reminder of old English life,
or any feature in more perfect harmony with its rural
surroundings, than a venerable old wooden windmill? Whether
standing on a far hilltop or on a gentle rise in the valley, its
place in the picture was always pleasing, often its centre of
attraction. In the opinion of Robert Louis Stevenson (*The
Foreigner at Home*) . . . .

> *"There are, indeed, few merrier spectacles than that of many
> windmills bickering together in a fresh breeze over a woody
> country; their halting alacrity of movement, their pleasant
> business, making bread all day with uncouth gesticulations, their
> air, gigantically human, as of a creature half alive, put a spirit of
> romance into the tamest landscape."*

Such romantic scenes live now only in pictures. Here, Walter
Rose (*The Village Carpenter*) describes the exhilaration he
experienced as a child, standing before those selfsame uncouth,
gesticulating sails . . . .

> *"The sails always reached to about two feet from the ground,
> and it was an enthralling experience to stand before them, as I
> often did, when a stiff wind was blowing, and watch them go
> roaring by: to note the 'swoop,' 'swoop' of each sail as it passed
> and to follow the orbit of one as it rose to almost sixty feet in the
> air, immediately to descend and swiftly pass again."*

In *Lettres de mon Moulin*, Alphonse Daudet reflects upon the disappearing windmill and the way of life that once centered upon it . . . .

> *"At one time there was a great milling trade, and from thirty miles around the people of the mas brought us their wheat to grind. . . .*
>
> *All about the village the hills were covered with windmills. Right and left your eye fell upon arms revolving in the mistral above the tops of the pine-trees, upon endless numbers of little donkeys laden with sacks, trotting up hill and down dale along the roads; and the whole week through it was a pleasure to hear on our hilltop the cracking of whips, the flapping of the arm-sails, and the 'gee-up' of the millers' boys. . . . On Sundays whole parties of us used to go up to the mills, where the millers treated us to Muscat wine. Their wives were like queens, decked out in all the bravery of their lace scarves and gold crosses. I used to bring my fife, and until black night there was dancing and farandoles. These mills, you see, were the joy and the wealth of our countryside.*
>
> *Unfortunately, some Frenchmen from Paris conceived the idea of establishing a big steam-driven mill on the Tarascon road. There's always a craze for anything new! People got into the habit of sending their corn to the steam mills, and the poor windmills were left without any work to do. For some time they tried to struggle on, but steam proved the stronger, and one after another, alas! they had to close down . . . . No more little donkeys. . . . The handsome millers' wives sold their gold crosses . . . . No more Muscat wine! No more farandole! . . ."*

Apart from Muscat and farandoles, a miller's life could be hard, as is portrayed by Julia Ewing in *Jan of the Windmill* . . . .

> *"In a coat and hat of painted canvas, he had been in and out ever since the storm began; now directing the two men who were*

working within, now struggling along the stage that ran outside the windmill, at no small risk of being fairly blown away.

He had reefed the sails twice already in the teeth of the blinding rain. But he did well to be careful. For it was in such a storm as this, five years ago 'come Michaelmas', that the worst of windmill calamities had befallen him, - the sails had been torn off his mill and dashed into a hundred fragments upon the ground. And such a mishap to a seventy feet tower mill means - as windmillers well know - not only a stoppage of trade, but an expense of two hundred pounds for the new sails . . . . That catastrophe had kept the windmiller a poor man for five years, and it gave him a nervous dread of storms."

The most famous episode in all of literature to feature windmills must surely be that which appears in Cervantes' novel *Don Quixote*. In one of his adventures, the Don imagines the sails of a group of windmills to be the waving arms of giants. This famous scene gives rise to the idiom "tilting at windmills", meaning to attack imaginary enemies or to fight futile battles. The word 'tilt', in this context, comes from jousting, which is precisely what the Don's fevered imagination leads to . . . .

"Just then they came in sight of thirty or forty windmills that rise from that plain. And no sooner did Don Quixote see them that he said to his squire, 'Fortune is guiding our affairs better than we ourselves could have wished. Do you see over yonder, friend Sancho, thirty or forty hulking giants? I intend to do battle with them and slay them. With their spoils we shall begin to be rich for this is a righteous war and the removal of so foul a brood from off the face of the earth is a service God will bless.'

'What giants?' asked Sancho Panza.

'Those you see over there,' replied his master, *'with their long arms. Some of them have arms well nigh two leagues in length.'*

'Take care, sir,' cried Sancho. *'Those over there are not giants but windmills. Those things that seem to be their arms are sails which, when they are whirled around by the wind, turn the millstone.'"*

Figure 12.1 Don Quixote tilting at a windmill, by Gustave Doré.

In poetry

More classical allusions to windmills appear in Shakespeare. In *Henry IV* Part I, Act 3, Harry Hotspur says to Mortimer, Earl of March . . . .

> ". . . . . *O! he's as tedious*
> *As a tired horse, a railing wife;*
> *Worse than a smoky house. I had rather live*
> *With cheese and garlic in a windmill, far,*
> *Than feed on cates and have him talk to me,*
> *In any summer-house in Christendom."*

But a cheese and garlic sandwich might go down remarkably well in a windmill, particularly if during the repast one can gaze down on acre upon acre of wheat, barley, oats or whatever, with a flock or herd grazing here or there and the odd farmhouse dotted about the patchwork sea of colour. Falstaff and his companions would surely have revelled to their heart's content in cheese and garlic perched in such a position, for in the second part of *Henry IV* Act 3, Justice Shallow remarks to this bulky man, who had "*a kind of alacrity in sinking*" . . . .

> "O, Sir John, do you remember since we all lay at night in the windmill in Saint George's Fields? . . . . Ha, it was a merry night!"

The Anglo-French writer Hilaire Belloc actually owned a working smock mill; Shipley Mill in Sussex formed part of an estate that he bought in 1905. Belloc employed a miller, and windmilling continued there until 1926. Thereafter he maintained the fabric but, following his death in 1953, the mill was found to be in a sad state of repair. It was then that friends raised money to restore it as a tribute to the writer.

Figure 12.2 A post mill in ruins.

Halnaker (pronounced Ha'nacker) Mill, the subject of this melancholy poem from 1912, stands on Halnaker Hill northeast of Chichester. In the poem, Belloc reflects on the collapse of the mill (struck by lightning), which he uses as a metaphor for the decay of the prevailing moral and social system.

HA'NACKER MILL

Sally is gone that was so kindly,
    Sally is gone from Ha'nacker Hill
And the Briar grows ever since then so blindly;
    And ever since then the clapper is still . . .
    And the sweeps have fallen from Ha'nacker Mill.

Ha'nacker Hill is in Desolation:
    Ruin a-top and a field unploughed.
And Spirits that call on a fallen nation,
    Spirits that loved her calling aloud,
    Spirits abroad in a windy cloud.
Spirits that call and no one answers -
    Ha'nacker's down and England's done.
Wind and Thistle for pipe and dancers,
    And never a ploughman under the Sun:
    Never a ploughman.   Never a one.

In *The Windmill*, Robert Bridges describes the miller *in situ*, account book in hand, thus laying emphasis on the commercial realities of a miller's life. His descriptive details with "creaking sails" and "shuddering timbers" conjure up a vision that anyone who has visited a working windmill will recognize.

THE WINDMILL

The green corn waving in the dale,
    The ripe grass waving on the hill:
I lean across the paddock pale
    And gaze upon the giddy mill.

153

Its hurtling sails a mighty sweep
   Cut thro' the air: with rushing sound
Each strikes in fury down the steep,
   Rattles, and whirls in chase around.

Beside his sacks the miller stands
   On high within the open door:
A book and pencil in his hands,
   His grist and meal he reckoneth o'er.

His tireless merry slave the wind
   Is busy with his work to-day:
From whencesoe'er he comes to grind ;
   He hath a will and knows the way.

He gives the creaking sails a spin,
   The circling millstones faster flee,
The shuddering timbers groan within,
   And down the shoots the meal runs free.

The miller giveth him no thanks,
   And doth not much his work o'erlook:
He stands beside the sacks, and ranks
   The figures in his dusty book.

Alfred Lord Tennyson follows Bridges' allusion to the miller's grip on the world of business. Here, he describes a prosperous and contented man, but one "full of dealings with the world". . . .

The Miller's Daughter

I see the wealthy miller yet,
   His double chin, his portly size,
And who that knew him could forget
   The busy wrinkles round his eyes?
The slow wise smile that, round about

His dusty forehead drily curl'd,
Seem'd half-within and half-without,
And full of dealings with the world?

As for the miller's daughter, the Laureate's feelings, tenderly expressed, are thus . . . .

It is the miller's daughter,
   And she is grown so dear, so dear,
That I would be the jewel
   That trembles in her ear:
For hid in ringlets day and night,
I'd touch her neck so warm and white . . .
. . . . And I would be the necklace,
   And all day long to fall and rise
Upon her balmy bosom,
   With her laughter or her sighs:
And I would lie so light, so light,
I scarce should be unclasp'd at night.

With so much grain in evidence, the risk of a vermin infested mill is a real problem. Here, Walter de la Mare pays recognition to the miller's countermeasure . . . .

FIVE EYES

In Hans' old mill his three black cats
Watch his bins for the thieving rats.
Whisker and claw, they crouch in the night,
Their five eyes smouldering green and bright:
Squeaks from the flour sacks, squeaks from where
The cold wind stirs on the empty stair,
Squeaking and scampering, everywhere.
Then down they pounce, now in, now out,
At whisking tail, and sniffing snout;
While lean old Hans he snores away

155

Till peep of light at break of day;
Then up he climbs to his creaking mill,
Out come his cats all grey with meal –
Jekkel, and Jessup, and one-eyed Jill.

. . . . and not to forget the source of the windmill's motive power; this by Christina Rossetti . . . .

WHO HAS SEEN THE WIND?

Neither I nor you.
But when the leaves hang trembling,
The wind is passing through.
Who has seen the wind?
Neither you nor I.
But when the trees bow down their heads,
The wind is passing by.

Reference was made in *Chapter 10* on Hawridge windmill, to the writer Gilbert Cannan who rented the mill after its conversion to private living accommodation. In his study at the very top of the mill, he wrote copiously, including a book of verse from which this extract is taken . . . .

ADVENTUROUS LOVE AND OTHER VERSES

I have a room wherein each day I sit
Word-weaving. I have windows south, east, west,
And with the changing sky my eyes are blest
Over this wide Heaven I let my wit
And fancy roam. My thoughts like birds do flit
Against the clouds in happy, happy quest
Of straws and twigs and moss to build their nest.
This is the spring when days with love are lit.

Amateur poets have also paid tribute to windmills. This anonymous sonnet pictures a feudal landlord and owner of a windmill - to which his tenants are obliged to take their grain - reflecting on his way of life, which is as idle as the slumbering landscape that surrounds him. He tries to create an *impression* of industry for the "bustling world" to see, but guilty conscience or not the landlord collects his toll, which his miller deducts "in kind".

THE LANDLORD'S TOLL.

I pause to gaze across the weald —
    There seems to be no life astir
    Save a skylark soaring in the air
Caroling o'er a wheat-filled field;
And on this landscape, patch-worked jade,
    Stillness lies; no other life is visible
    But the slow-winding sails of my old windmill
Play flitting change with sun and shade.
In this place I follow my idle way,
    As the bustling world would judge it,
Like a windmill I twirl my arms all day
    For the sake of looking fitted —
      Though I toil not for what we grind
      The miller mulcts my toll in kind!

James Edwin Saunders was a miller from Slough. He died in 1935, aged 91, after a lifetime spent in windmilling that brought him immense satisfaction in spite of once being on the brink of bankruptcy. James kept a diary in which his conflicts and consolations are recorded, mostly in rhyme; one of his long poems, which sums up his feelings for his craft, begins . . . .

MUSIC OF THE MILL

There is poetry in Milling, when one's heart is free
From the care that blinds one's vision - oft 'twas so with me
To a large extent, though even in those anxious days
There were times when I had glimpses of its transient rays.
How I like to see good running and due pleasure found
In the Mill's efficient working, as I walked around.
When I went to bed I saw it still before my eye,
Still I heard the music stealing like a lullaby,
Soothing me to sleep and dreamland like an evening psalm,
After days of busy effort, like a restful balm.

Another amateur poet, H E Howard from Chesham, wrote *50 Poems of Buckinghamshire*. A few lines from the beginning of one of these poems, written in 1935 . . . .

HAWRIDGE COMMON

At noon among the rolling hills I strayed
And watched the bearded ploughman. In the
    vale
The February sun sang out and strayed
Up o'er the bramble slope until the sail
Of that old windmill tried to live again.
The wind tip-toed on every blade of grass;
And shimmering ponds as smooth
    as smoothest glass.

The last poem needs little introduction, for it must be the best known of what windmill poems there are, and one of Henry Wadsworth Longfellow's most enduring . . . .

THE WINDMILL

Behold! a giant am I!
　Aloft here in my tower,
　With my granite jaws I devour
The maize, and the wheat, and the rye,
　And grind them into flour.

I look down over the farms;
　In the fields of grain I see
　The harvest that is to be,
And I fling to the air my arms,
　For I know it is all for me.

I hear the sound of flails
　Far off, from the threshing-floors
　In barns, with their open doors,
And the wind, the wind in my sails,
　Louder and louder roars.

I stand here in my place,
　With my foot on the rock below,
　And whichever way it may blow
I meet it face to face,
　As a brave man meets his foe.

And while we wrestle and strive
　My master, the miller, stands
　And feeds me with his hands;
For he knows who makes him thrive,
　Who makes him lord of lands.

On Sundays I take my rest;
Church-going bells begin
Their low, melodious din;
I cross my arms on my breast,
And all is peace within.

Windmills and symbolism

Not just in Spanish literature, but in many other cultures, the windmill has acquired symbolism with a host of different meanings. For example, in China the wearing of a piece of jewelry depicting a windmill represents a blowing away of bad luck and a change of fortune for the better.

In the Roman Catholic Church, the windmill is the symbol of the martyrdom of St. Victor of Marseilles, a solider of the Roman army who was killed in AD 290 for exhorting local Christians to be firm in their faith. For this he was put to death by being crushed under a millstone.

Perhaps the best known modern literary analogy is George Orwell's warning of the failure of the Communist system, which he satirized so powerfully in his novel *Animal Farm*. Orwell used the windmill to represent Stalin's 'Five-Year Plan', which aimed to improve Soviet industry for the benefit of the proletariats. Just like the eventual fate of the windmill in the book, Stalin's plan was an utter failure. When the windmill in *Animal Farm* was blown down in a storm due to being built with shoddy materials, the animals decide to build another, just as Stalin kept introducing new Five-Year Plans. The final destruction of the windmill became known as 'The Battle of Windmill', which Orwell used to represent the real-life Battle of Stalingrad.

THE MILLER OF TRING

Lyrics by Herbert Brandon

Born in Tring in 1878, Herbert J Brandon first lived in Akeman Street and attended a Non-conformist boys' school in Park Road. As a young man he worked in the family furnishing business, filling his spare time by writing numerous song lyrics - often to music by Horace Keats - prose pieces and stories, many of which were published both in England and Australia (the great Australian baritone Peter Dawson recorded Brandon's song, *Drake's Call*). The lyrics for *The Miller of Tring* appeared in 1917, possibly in an effort to provide some cheer in the darkest days of WWI. Brandon lived in Tring all his life; he died in 1945.

THE MILLER OF TRING.

Song

Words by
HERBERT J. BRANDON.

Music by

BARTON CHARLES.

Copyright MCMXVII,
by West & Co.

Price 2/ net

LONDON
WEST
& Co

24 RATHBONE PLACE,
OXFORD STREET, W.

This Song may be Sung in Public without Fee or License, except at Theatres & Music Halls.

THE MILLER OF TRING.

Words by
HERBERT J. BRANDON.

Music by
BARTON CHARLES.

There once was a Miller, a Miller of Tring, And he was as blithe as the birds in the Spring, Each morning he rose with the song of the lark, And he car-olled as gai-ly un-til it was dark. Full many a maiden that pass'd by the Mill, Would

This song may be sung in public without fee or license except at Theatres and Music Halls.

Copyright MCMXVII by West & Co.

W. & Co. 7184.

slower.

stop for a gossip with heart-y good-will, And nev-er a lassie but gave him a smile, Tho' a

Batch-e-lor still he re-main'd all the while.

Ped. *Ped.*

With joviality and in strict time.

And the Miller day by day sang this merry roundelay, Of blithe and bonny lasses there are

plen-ty, But if I were fain to wed I must live a-lone in-stead, For the

W. & Co. 2121.

slower.

though all the lasses for him had a smile Yet a Batch.e.lor still he re.main'd _____ all the

while. _____ And the Mill.ler day by day sang this mer.ry rounde.lay, Of

blithe and bon.ny lasses there are plen.ty, But if I were fain to wed, I must

live a.lone in.stead, For the lass.es that I love are more than twen . ty.

Chapter 13

LOCAL WINDMILLS TO VISIT

Pitstone post mill

Location: near to the junction of the B488 and B489;
OS Sheet 165; SP 945 157; telephone 01442 851227

Pitstone mill (*plates 1-3*) is described in *Chapter 7*. Although in mechanical working order, the mill is now a static exhibit managed by the National Trust. It may be approached and viewed from the outside at any time, but public openings are restricted to Sunday and Bank Holiday afternoons during the summer months. Please confirm opening times before visiting.

Brill post mill

Location: about ½ mile N.W. of the town centre;
OS Sheet 165; SP 652 142; tel 01296 382389

A 17th century post mill, similar in style and vintage to that at Pitstone and possibly by the same millwright. The windmill (*plates 4-6*) stands on open ground at the end of Windmill Street, its elevated situation giving a fine view of the surrounding countryside. It may be approached and viewed from the outside at any time, but public openings are restricted to Sunday afternoons during the summer months. Please confirm opening times before visiting.

Lacey Green smock mill

Location: behind 'The Whip' public house;
OS Sheet 165; SP 819 008; tel 01844 275871

Lacey Green smock mill (*plates 10-14*) lies about two miles south-east of Princes Risborough. It is believed to date from 1650, making it Britain's oldest smock mill. Judging by old photographs, the mill was in a ruinous and derelict condition in 1970, but has since been restored, quite miraculously, by a dedicated team of windmill preservationists. The windmill is open to the public on Sundays and Bank Holiday Mondays, from May to September, and operates on some occasions. Please confirm opening times before visiting.

Quainton tower mill

Location: off Upper Street, N. of town centre;
OS Sheet 165; SP 746 202; tel 01296 655306

Also known as Banner Mill, this 6-storey, brick-built tower mill (*plates 26-28*) dates from 1832. It remained in operation as a windmill until 1881 when steam replaced wind power; milling had ceased altogether by 1900. Under the tender care of the Quainton Windmill Society, the derelict mill was restored over a period of 23 years, returning to full operation in 1997. The windmill, which overlooks the picturesque village green, is open on Sunday mornings throughout the year and operates when wind conditions are favourable. The *George and Dragon* public house (on the Green) serves food, while the nearby Quainton Railway Centre is another place of interest worth a visit. Please confirm opening times before visiting.

Chinnor post mill

Location: in Mill Lane (junction B4009 & B4445); OS Sheet 165; SP 749 010; telephone Adrian Marshall, 01844 292095.

Chinnor post mill (*plates 7-9*) was built in 1789 and ground wheat into flour until 1923. By 1967 she was derelict and was pulled down to make way for housing. Fortunately, much of the structure was saved and the mill is presently being reconstructed on a site near to its original home by a dedicated team of volunteers.

The mill's construction is unusual, it having three (rather than the usual two) cross-trees, which require six 'quarter bars' and brick piers. Curved struts support a curb ring that stabilizes the bottom of the *buck* (superstructure).

A visit to Chinnor mill provides a valuable opportunity to see a post mill in the course of construction and to inspect the post, quarter bars and piers, which are often difficult to see clearly when enclosed in a roundhouse. The mill is open on alternate Sundays 10.00-14.00, but can be viewed externally at any time.

APPENDIX: windmills not open to the public

Edlesborough tower mill

Location about ¼ mile N.W. of Edlesborough Hill;
OS Sheet 165; SP 982 192.

Edlesborough tower mill (*plate 29*), also known as Simmons mill after the family who owned it over many generations, is located on the eastern side of the village on the Ouzel, astride the Bucks/Beds border. A private drive leads to the mill, which is not visible from the highway. The owner believes the mill was built c.1790; the only references to it appear in *A History of the County of Bedford*: Volume 3 (1912) . . . .

> *"The village* [Edlesborough] *is watered by numerous streams, which rise at Well Head and on the Dunstable Downs, and find their way eventually to the Ouzel, which forms the western boundary. On its banks, slightly north of Edlesborough Hill, stands Edlesborough Mill. Steam is employed here when insufficiency of water prevents that power being utilized. On the other side of the stream, in Buckinghamshire, is an old windmill, whose sails were blown down seventeen years ago* [c.1895]."

. . . . and in *English Windmills* Vol. II. (1932), which records that . . . . *"it has no sails and is derelict"*; photographic evidence (*fig. 13.1*) certainly bears this out. The present owner has restored the body of the mill, which now stands in carefully tended grounds, nicely set off against the Ouzel and the landscaped millpond and mill race of its former neighbour, the watermill - a delight to see. Today, the old windmill is serving its retirement as a holiday home to let.

Figure 13.1 Edlesborough tower mill prior to restoration. The former
steam and water mills are in the background.

Doolittle combined wind and water mill

Location on Doolittle Lane 1¼ miles S.E. of Eaton Bray church.
OS Sheet 165; SP 990 202.

Doolittle mill (*plate 30*) is thought to have been built between
1815 and 1825. It is a rare example of a combined wind and
water mill, the water mill being situated in the first two floors
with the windmill in the brick tower above. The windmill
ceased operation in 1868 when its sails were blown off and a
steam engine was then installed. It closed in 1921. Today, the
mill is a private dwelling with some commercial premises
situated in the grounds. It can be seen from the public highway.

Figure 13.2 Doolittle combined mill (pre-1868).

Local folklore has it that Doolittle mill acquired its name - a corruption of "Do Little" - because it is sited at the head of a stream and hence, in dry weather when water flow was low, the water mill was not capable of doing much work. It was then that recourse was made to its sails and, later, to the steam engine.

COLOUR PLATES

Pitstone post mill

Plate 1 Pitstone post mill.

Plate 2 Centrifugal governor, Pitstone post mill.

174

Plate 3 Windshaft and brake wheel, Pitstone post mill. The chain extending to the pulley at the top of the picture drives the auxiliary shaft, which powers the sack hoist and other ancillary machinery.

Plate 4 Brill post mill.

Plate 5 Brake wheel, wallower and (*under-driven*) stones, Brill post mill.

176

Plate 6 Brill post mill: the main post and (above it) the crown-tree, which support the buck (the mill's superstructure). The meal bin is to the right of the post and just visible at its top left is the great spur wheel.

177

Plate 7 Chinnor post mill in course of reconstruction.

Plate 8 Cast iron windshaft and poll (nearest the camera). Chinnor post mill.

Plate 9 Chinnor post mill: main post, quarter bars, cross-trees and piers. This mill is unusual in having three (rather than two) cross-trees and six (rather then four) 'quarter' bars and brick piers. The ring stabilizes the buck (superstructure).

Plate 10 Lacey Green smock mill. Two sweeps in full sail; two, three-quarter.

Plate 11 Internal structure of a smock mill. The large timbers are *cant posts*.

Plate 12 Brake wheel and wallower, Lacey Green smock mill.

Plate 13 Upright shaft and its bearing, Lacey Green smock mill.

181

Plate 14 Great spur wheel (top left) and stone nut (top centre), Lacey Green smock mill. Millstones driven from above are described as *over-driven*.

Plate 15 Hawridge tower mill.

Plate 16 Iron windshaft and brake wheel, Hawridge tower mill.

Plate 17 Iron windshaft and roller bearing, Hawridge tower mill.

Plate 18 *Gilbert Cannan and his Mill* (Hawridge tower mill),
by Mark Gertler. Now in the Ashmolean Museum, Oxford.

Plate 19 Goldfield tower mill, Tring.

186

Plate 20 The cap, Golfield tower mill, Tring.

Plate 21 Great spur wheel, Goldfield tower mill, Tring. Iron to wood coupling, seen here, ran more smoothly and was cheaper to maintain than iron to iron.

Plate 22 The great octagonal tower mill at Wendover.

Plate 23 Looking up at the apex of the cap, Wendover mill.

189

Plate 24 The curb, Wendover mill. Three rollers are visible just above the rack.

Plate 25 The iron windshaft and its bearing, Wendover mill.
The casting in the centre of the shaft carried the brake wheel.

Plate 26 Quainton tower mill. The twist in the sails gives better performance.

Plates 27 and 28 Quainton tower mill: the worm gear above, when driven by the fantail (top right, plate 26), rotates the cog and its spindle. The spindle terminates on the pinion, shown below, which in turn engages with the rack that extends around the perimeter of the cap. Through this system of gearing, the fantail drives the cap to face the sails into the wind.

Plates 29 and 30 Edlesborough and Doolittle mills.

GLOSSARY OF MILLING TERMS.

BEDSTONE: the lower of a pair of millstones, which remains stationary.

BINS: wooden boxes for holding the grain.

BIN FLOOR: floor of mill where the grain bins are situated.

BRAKE: wooden or iron brake shoe encircling the brake wheel.

BRAKE WHEEL: the largest gear wheel, fixed on the windshaft. The brake contracts onto its wooden rim.

BRAN: partly ground husk of grain. The outer coating of a grain of wheat, rye, barley, or corn.

BREAST: front of a post mill.

BRIDGE: metal bar cemented into eye of runner stone to act as bearing for the top of the spindle.

BUCK: the body of a post mill.

CANISTER: see Poll End.

CANT POSTS: corner posts of a mill.

CAP: the revolving top of a tower or smock mill.

CENTRE or MAIN POST: the large central post which supports a post mill.

CHAIN WHEEL: wheel turned by means of an endless chain. For winding mill or for working striking gear.

CILL: low stone or brick wall.

COGS: the wooden teeth (usually applewood) inserted into cast gear wheel to drive mill machinery.

COMMON SAILS: sails with a wooden framework covered by canvas.

COMPOSITION STONE:	millstone made from cement and carborundum.
CURB:	circular track at the top of the tower or smock mill on which the cap turns.
CROSS:	multi-armed iron casting fixed to the end of the windshaft to carry the sails.
CROSSTREES:	horizontal timbers at right angles which support the centre post of a post mill.
EYE:	hole in the centre of the runner stone through which grain passes into the middle of the two stones.
FANTAIL:	a small windmill which is used to keep a windmill facing into the wind automatically.
FAN STAGE:	platform at the rear of the cap of a smock or tower mill to provide access to the fantail fan at rear of cap which automatically turns it to face the wind.
FEED SHOE:	guides grain from hopper into eye of stone.
FLOUR DRESSER:	machine for separating flour from the rest of the meal.
FRENCH BURR:	freshwater quartz stone from France used to mill wheat.
FURROWS:	low part of pattern on the surface of millstones.
GALLERY:	a platform around the cap.
GOVERNOR:	automatic device which adjusts the distance between the stones as the sails turn faster or slower.
GREAT SPUR WHEEL:	large gear wheel on the upright shaft driving the stone nuts.
GRIST:	the blend of different wheats a miller selects to make flour. Most flours are made from a mixture of wheats.

196

HEAD WHEEL:	is carried on the windshaft in a post mill and has a brake around its circumference. It drives a stone nut.
LANDS:	high parts of pattern on the surfaces of millstones.
LUFFING:	see winding.
MIDDLINGS:	the coarsest part of the wheat meal ground by a mill; the last product excepting the bran remaining after finer grades of flour are sifted out.
MILL-BILL:	a chisel-ended tool used for dressing or sharpening the grinding surface of a millstone.
MILLSTONE GRIT:	the name given to the rock quarried in Yorkshire and Derbyshire, and used in making Peak or Grey millstones.
MILLING SOKE:	the manorial law governing ownership, building and usage of mills.
MILLER'S TOLL:	the portion of ground meal retained by the miller as payment for his services. It tended to vary between one tenth and one twentieth, with one-sixteenth being common.
MILLWRIGHT:	a craftsman who erected and maintained milling machinery. Early millwrights were specialist carpenters who at the start of the Industrial Revolution were pressed into service to build the earliest powered textile mills.
OVERDRIFT:	stones driven from above.
PATENT SAILS:	shuttered sails with self-regulating control gear to adjust their speed automatically.
PEAK STONE:	millstone grit from the Peak District of Derbyshire used for grinding animal feeds.
PETTICOAT:	downward extension of the cap to cover the top of the tower against the weather.

PIERS:	brick supports of a trestle.
POLL END:	a cast iron socket at the end of the windshaft to hold the stocks.
POST MILL:	a type of mill in which the body of the mill pivots about a central upright timber post to enable the sails to be faced into the wind ("winded").
ROLLER MILL:	a mill in which fluted metal rollers are used in place of millstones.
ROLLER REEFING SAILS:	use a canvas strip wound around a roller in place of shutters. The mill does not have to be stopped in order to adjust the sails.
ROUNDHOUSE:	building around the trestle of a post mill to protect it and provide storage.
RUNNER STONE:	top stone of a pair which is turned by the mill.
SAILS:	the source of power in a windmill. They are carried on the windshaft. Most windmills had four sails, although some had five, six or even eight.
SCOURER:	a machine used to separate usable grain from debris such as dirt, dust, and chaff.
SEPARATOR:	a machine used to separate grain from other foreign objects, such as rocks, weeds, and twigs.
SHUTTERS:	a series of hinged vanes in vertical rows in spring and patent sails.
SMOCK MILL:	mill with wooden tower, often on a stone or brick base, with a revolving cap.
SMUTTER:	removes the black spots of smut caused by a fungus disease that can grow on grain if its gets damp.
SPIDER:	metal coupling operating the shutters of patent sails.
SPRING SAILS:	sails with shutters linked to a spring, the tension of

which can be set manually so that the shutters will open and close according to wind strength.

STAGING: a platform around the body of the mill.

STOCKS: heavy timbers to which the sails are fitted.

STONE DRESSER: a man whose profession it is to re-sharpen (or dress) millstones.

STONE FLOOR: the floor of the mill on which the millstones are located.

STONE NUT: final gear at top of quant which drives the stones.

STRIKING GEAR: mechanism to open and close the shutters on sails.

SWEEPS: the term sometimes used to describe the sails.

TAIL: the rear end of a post mill.

TAIL POLE: a long timber at the rear of a post mill or cap used to turn it manually.

TAIL WHEEL: wheel mounted at rear of windshaft to drive a second set of stones.

TAIL WINDING: when a wind catches the sails from the rear; a strong tail wind has been known to blow the cap off the tower.

TALTHUR: small beam attached to tail pole which when hooked to the ladder will lift it clear of the ground while the mill is being winded.

TENTERING GEAR: device to make fine adjustments to the gap between the millstones.

TOWER MILL: mill with a brick tower and revolving cap.

TRESTLE: wooden substructure of a post mill supporting the main post.

TUN CASE:	see VAT
UNDERDRIFT:	stones driven from beneath.
VANES:	blades of a fantail.
VAT:	removable wooden case enclosing millstones.
WALLOWER:	horizontal gearwheel at top of upright shaft taking drive directly from the brake wheel.
WHIP:	the backbone of a sail or sweep.
WINDBOARD:	wide board replacing the shutters on inner half of leading edge of sails.
WINDING:	process of turning sails into the eye of the wind.
WINDSHAFT:	main axle of iron or wood that carries the sails and brake wheel.

SOURCES

Austin, Wendy

Tring Personalities (2000)

The Second Tring Collection (2007)

Davis, Jean — *Aldbury the Open Village (1987)*

Fairbairn, Sir William — *Treatise on Mills and Millwork (1865)*

Farnell, Mary — *The Account Books of William Cooper, Millwright of Aylesbury (held by Buckinghamshire Record Office together with the ledgers)*

Farr, Diana — *Gilbert Cannan: A Georgian Prodigy (1978)*

Freese, Stanley — *Windmills of Buckinghamshire* (collated notes, mostly dating from the 1930s, held in the Centre for Buckinghamshire Local Studies, Aylesbury)

Freese, Stanley — *Windmills and Millwrighting (1957)*

Hopkins, F.T., Freese, Stanley. — *In Search of Windmills (1931)*

Jones, Ken — *Chiltern Windmills (1972)*

Moore, Cyril — *Hertfordshire Windmills and Windmillers (1999)*

Rose, Walter — *The Village Carpenter (1937)*

Smith, Arthur C. — *Windmills of Hertfordshire (1972)*

Smith, Donald — *English Windmills, Vol. II (1932)*

Summervell, Samuels, Mead, and Eckett — *The Book of Wendover (1989)*

Wailes, Rex — *The English Windmill (1954)*

Wray, David — *Pitstone Windmill (1976)*

. . . . also . . . .

Guide to Quainton Windmill, Bernard Hall (2007).

Notes on Marsworth Mill compiled by Mrs M Bellhouse (2005).

Notes on the history of Pitstone (Brook End) Mill by Keith Russell (2009).

National Census Records 1841 - 1901.

Trade directories 1823 - 1930.

The Bucks Herald archives.

The Bucks Advertiser & Aylesbury News archives.

Hertfordfordshire Countryside archives.

The Berkhamsted Gazette, 24 December 1954.

OS maps and others as credited in the text.